TWO,
THREE,
MANY
MORE

*"How close and bright would the future
appear if two, three, many Vietnams
flowered on the face of the globe . . ."*
—Che Guevara

*"The goal written on the university
walls was 'Create two, three,
many Columbias'. . ."*
—Tom Hayden

BOOKS BY NICHOLAS VON HOFFMAN

Mississippi Notebook
The Multiversity
We Are the People Our Parents Warned Us Against
Two, Three, Many More

TWO, THREE, MANY MORE

A NOVEL

NICHOLAS VON HOFFMAN

Chicago   QUADRANGLE BOOKS

Library of Congress Catalog Card Number: 69-20164

To my mother and my father

The only real characters in this book are the ones with real names. I would like to thank Susan Dooley for editorial help and Mrs. Margaret Weiskopf, who typed the manuscript.

TWO,
THREE,
MANY
MORE

THEY KNEW EVERYTHING. They knew what they didn't know. They knew what isn't known, what isn't knowable. But what they knew couldn't serve them. They knew that also.

Together they had taken communion in times past. Then they had been a fraternal corporation joined in awareness of themselves as a people set apart for special work and a unique life. Not so long ago they had come in procession from their campus, the beaux-arts cockpit, robed and cowled in the colors of art, law, medicine, philosophy, each carrying a daffodil against a wet and foggy April morning, displaying the solidarity of their order for peace, proclaiming against the war, making their petition, their petition, their petition.

They had come, a gowned column of thousands—Nobel laureates, deans of every science, of every art, deans of students, of graduate studies and divinity, professors and doctors of all the skills, disciplines, and crafts, followed by the young masters, the teaching assistants, the undergraduates, the editors of the university press, the staff of the student health service, the counselors in the admissions office, the part-time secretaries and the full-time wives from the bursar's office, imploring no more war. They had assembled in the Square below the steps of the Minerva, Mother of Knowledge, statue and had marched out Manion Gate across the slum to meet the processions from the other colleges and universities and, holding their daffodils, they had filled the lakeside amphitheater and listened to Martin Luther King.

Their own numbers had moved them to solemnity and silence. They had been made happy in themselves, in their closeness, in their size and their importance as an order. Men and women of mind modified by informed analysis, by studied, qualified knowledge, they knew they would not stop the war, knew how the world is run, but they also believed they would be heard. Weren't they the world's most necessary people? When King had finished speaking and the We Shall Overcome had been sung, the war went on and they ceased to be a unitary body. Their order became divided. They never took communion together again.

At the Center for Applied Technology they worked on their new polymer—it would replace steel. The electric typewriters in the International Relations Institute made clean copies with justified right-hand margins of memoranda—of what? And at the Flexner Research Hospital a resident was on duty to sniff out and seize the hearts from the bodies of hit-and-run victims, while the chiefs meditated on the advantages of the first human brain transplant. Hundreds of classes met in the right rooms with the right instructors in precise accordance with the catalogue. People said people were waiting for an action.

When it came, they did not like it, said it was eccentric, stupid, apolitical. It was a contribution to what Myron

Mirsky called "our unstable equilibrium." At least once a week Mirsky, the social scientist, made the remark over lunch at the Faculty Club. "First Berkeley, then Columbia, next it's us. You don't have to believe me. We will be put up against the wall by history."

When the action came it was static: the overweight Roysterman chained to five others in the sanctuary of University Chapel. They were standing upright with miscellaneous activist women at their feet when they were discovered and displayed on local television, making statements that they were in conscience bound to resist the war any way they could. Several professors from the Divinity School had come over to approve Roysterman and the others manacling themselves to the boy, who said he was seeking asylum after refusing induction into the army.

The boy, David somebody or other, wasn't a student at the university; he'd simply come claiming his asylum and making short, declaratory statements. Roysterman wouldn't say much either, except, "I'm here in the role of a supportive, anonymous witness. . . . I'm doing what David asked me to do. I'm not going to say anything." And David couldn't say much, so the action lacked focus for the first twenty-four hours, while the federal authorities insisted they'd never heard of David and that he could stand there chained to the Protestant chaplain as long as he liked.

Shapiro, the leading undergraduate radical, came to look at them in sanctuary, lit only by the spotlights which aimed at the altar. Scratching curly hair with two hands, Shapiro talked loud enough so the six had to hear him: "This isn't a political action."

"It's an action. It should be supported," said his friend.

"So what do we do? Everybody come and sit down all over the church and we have a confrontation. With who? The cops? The cops didn't start the war. The power structure did. I want a confrontation with the power structure. These people are egomaniacs. Ministers and peaceniks with personal problems."

"So what're you going to do? Call another meeting?"

The six clanked and sat down. They were chained, so they had to move in unison. They didn't answer Shapiro, who continued the two-handed scratching of his hair as he left with his friend. Others came to look: Roger Elias, the teaching assistant in mathematics; Myron Mirsky, to be sure the story in the *Daily Review* was correct; some assistant deans, and, in the end, four federal marshals with hacksaws: the government had found David's file. They sawed his chains off and then one of them asked, "Please don't go limp. You're a big boy, a lot for four middle-aged men to carry."

"No, I won't go limp. Going limp is a covertly violent act. I'm non-violent and non-cooperative. I only want you to understand that I'm not going limp because I don't feel hostile toward you. I do not even feel hostile toward the system, but I won't cooperate with it."

The marshals told him he was a good boy and walked him out, leaving Roysterman and the others still chained and clanking together.

"No, I'm not wrong. I didn't say that incident at the chapel would be it. I don't know when it will be. We won't know when it is until it's here, but it's not yet," said Myron Mirsky at the Faculty Club the next day.

"Myron, you're an apocalyptic intellectual. You feed off the mood of approaching disaster, but your poetical processes aren't reality," his tablemate said. He looked around the room and derived assurance from the undergraduate men in white coats bussing the dishes back into the kitchen.

"I'm a Jew. I know. It's up against the wall with this university. I know it. If I didn't know it, I'd take the offer from UCLA and get out of here, but the Jew who tells me what's going to happen makes me stay and wait to participate in it."

"Oh, Christ, Myron."

"Unh-unh, wrong god."

There was no television to display the action that followed Roysterman's. The napalm demonstration was photographed, however, and several pictures were printed in the *Daily Review*. Some of Shapiro's friends put on the performance at noon in front of the Minerva. There were three of them, one dressed in a white smock, another in what purported to be a general's uniform (with little red plastic airplanes instead of stars sewn on the shoulders), and a third in a business suit. They looked so crazy dancing on the granite stones that a larger-than-usual crowd gathered to watch. Science (the white smock) raised the bottle of napalm over his head like a priest with a chalice.

"Burn yourself, creep!" shouted a boy who had big shoulders and a sport coat and was taken to be a jock by the radicals.

Unheeding, Science went on with the skit. "Better napalm with the new additive KC19. Soon this new discovery will be put to work in civilian life in the engines of your automobiles to reduce harmful carbon deposits and to make your teeth bright!"

"Soon, soon, soon," chanted the general and the businessman.

"First, though, KC19, the new miracle additive, must go to war to defend freedom," Science said, and the chorus agreed. "Defend freedom, defend freedom."

"Against aggression," said Science.

"Defend freedom against aggression," chanted the businessman and the general.

"Defend freedom against communism and beards," said Science, while the businessman and the general dug into a box and came out with a fat, white dove, whose wings and legs had been trussed. The sport-coat-and-shoulders made for the base of the Minerva. He hit the general so hard one of the plastic planes took off from an epaulette, but he was too slow to stop the action. Science had poured the napalm on the dove and ignited it.

"KC19," Science intoned.

"For your car," said the businessman.

"For your teeth," said the general, picking up his plane.

The action provoked reaction—not aimed to retaliate at the performers, however. Dean Robertson of the College, when asked by a troubled faculty member if he was going to do anything, took the position that it was a matter for the Animal Welfare League. The incineration of a live dove on the pedestal of Minerva broke no University regulations that he was aware of, but it caused an uneasiness among some of the older people, a certain second look into the eyes of youth. Nothing was said. Even Mirsky at the Faculty Club failed to comment on the episode. A week later there was a letter in the *Daily Review:*

TO THE EDITOR:

The killing of a bird is a small matter. I'm ashamed even to write about it, knowing, as we all do, how human beings are killed every day in the war. When I look at the news on television and see people dying from napalm on the screen, only to have their expiring breath interrupted for a dog food commercial, it even occurs to me that killing all our pets in a bloody expiatory gesture would be a pardonable act. I sympathize with the young men who performed the immolation on the steps of the statue the other day. I venture to say I have opposed the war as long and as vehemently as they, at least I hope I have, but I'm disturbed, nonetheless. It's not the thing itself I object to; it's the edge on it. The act suggests a capacity for frightfulness which frankly scares me. Perhaps it's the war that has agitated such capacities within us. Perhaps this is another cost the war exacts from us. If it is, it may be the most serious of all.

E. J. CORNFORD, Professor of English

Shapiro read the letter and told his friend, Sil, who'd played Science in the skit, that he hated liberals. "Radicalize them," Sil had responded.

"How?" Shapiro asked.

It was a truism with all political thinkers on the campus that an action, many actions, would radicalize liberals, but still there were none. At the SDS chapter meetings, the question was taken up every time without resolution. The arguments were long and inconclusive, and the longer they became, the fewer the people who came to the meetings. The boy who made side money stringing for *Time* reported in the magazine's survey round-up of campuses that "the movement" was all but dead at the University. Then Henry Hungerford banned Mungo from speaking on the campus.

"I didn't even believe it when I heard it," Myron Mirsky said. "I knew Hungerford wasn't very bright, but I still can't believe that McVey, Robertson, somebody couldn't have gotten to him. It's ridiculous. I'm embarrassed to call it an academic freedom issue. Why, nobody would have even come to listen to Mungo. Another black man with an identity crisis, and such a crisis! Can you imagine getting yourself arrested for conspiring to blow the ass off the Statue of Liberty?"

Today's lunch partner took the down side for a change. "Well, Myron, you've been saying something would happen. Maybe this is our Berkeley."

"No, it's too silly. It's the kind of racism you can't get indignant over. It's the innocent, hysterical kind that our University president gets every time he drives through the slum that has us pinned down on three sides," Mirsky explained. As he talked he warmed to a sarcastic, mocking hilarity. Very different from the soft-voiced crispness he employed when he'd say, "Up against the wall with you, University. History is putting the stick up on you."

"Did you read Hungerford's statement? It didn't sound like that, and there was a lawyer-like consistency about it."

Mirsky kept nodding as he heard the question. As soon as it was over he expanded his disquisition: "Very lawyer-like, but silly. Hungerford is scared by black men, even without them raping an occasional coed or faculty wife or stabbing a University guard. It's a simple terror, no guilt about it. Even now, not even yet, does he realize he's been stealing the black man's territory from him for ten years. He really believes that *cordon sanitaire* of parks and labs he's building around this place is 'institutional expansion.'

"See, if he knew anything, as president the last person he'd be scared of is Mungo. Maybe in the end Mungo will be very dangerous because nobody understands him. Hungerford thinks he's some kind of elemental force, a conspirator, guerrilla chieftain for the urban house-to-house wars. That's because he runs around in a dashiki with an Afro haircut. Even the white boys with beards on his own campus scare Hungerford. So I grant you, if our learned president does this kind of thing often enough, Mungo'll mean trouble just because he's misunderstood. Misunderstood also by our baby-faced radicals. They think he's an avenging black man, too. Essentially, or just with a few twists, they think he's what Hungerford thinks he is."

"Well, what is he?"

"He's on the Mayor's payroll. He's a theatrical politician, a shattered, indecisive personality with a mouth, a great mouth. All these blacks are marvelous preachers. I have a student whose thesis topic is black rhetoric. You should hear the tapes. That's all Mungo is. Indecisive, a braggart, with a band of welfare mothers and the least dangerous adolescents in the ghetto. Big Black Cats! Everybody equates them with the Black Panthers, but they're not. Can you imagine a man who gets drunk and lets a police *agent provocateur* talk him into a conspiracy to blow the fanny off the Statue of Liberty? That's when they got him, that's when the famous Mr. Mungo became the Mayor's man. They're holding that silly indictment over his head with one hand and paying him just enough to live on with the other. It's absurd. A man like that comes parading around Manion Gate with his bullhorn and his loud talk and Martin Hungerford thinks one of the world's great universities is in imminent danger of being sacked and burned. But that shows you where we are. We're so tense, so worried, so overmythologized, so helpless in the face of our avenging obsessions that bad things can happen. But not Mungo, not Mungo."

"How do you know so much about Mungo?"

"I'm a social scientist—and what's that? It's a gossip with reliable information."

The ban against Mungo lasted seventy-two hours, long enough to bring to life three petitions signed by a large number of the instructional staff and one good, major picketing. The action was directed against Hungerford's office and was led not by Shapiro but by Young Democrats and Republicans and a whole gang from the student government, including even the little girl who ran the Star Office, the reticule in the student bureaucracy that hired name entertainers for the big dances. There were secretaries from half a dozen deans' offices on the line, and several deans came out personally to smile.

"Liberals," said Shapiro.

Sil wouldn't be bothered coming over to the Square to look.

The fat Roysterman was there with his wife, a pretty young woman who alarmed people by giving off symptoms which suggested forms of piety they'd only read about. It wasn't communion and it didn't move Roysterman. He had been at Selma, and the validity of all politics was measured against that experience. What he saw marching around in front of

Fletcher Hall was a sunshine crowd with no tension. He stayed to support it, even walked on the line for a bit, but it did nothing for him. His religion was a search for the most awful kinds of nervous intensities.

At the end of seventy-two hours of good-natured indigna-tion, a statement issued itself out of Fletcher Hall. It came via the Public Information Office, signed by A. A. McVey, chancellor of the University, and it read as though it had been drafted by a pack of lawyers and gymnasts. First it said the University had always been strong for free speech, debate, and dissent, and the chancellor hoped and prayed it always would be. Then it said the reason Mungo was refused permission to speak on campus was because he had announced he was coming to recruit for the Big Black Cats, not to trade in the marketplace of ideas. That wouldn't do. The Big Black Cats was an off-campus organization which had never been approved by the Dean of Students, so it had no standing at the University and no right to use its facilities. But: "Arleigh Wickersham, chairman of the political science department, has invited Mr. Mungo to take part in the graduate seminar on the new politics which, due to the importance of the topic and the interest in Mr. Mungo, will be open to all who care to attend."

So Mungo was gotten off the Square to be housed and hedged inside. He never made it to any of the seminars, and he wasn't missed. He had nothing to say you couldn't hear on television, whenever they were moved to do one of their tell-it-like-it-is documentaries. He had provided the picketers with a degree of righteous satisfaction, while the statement had provided Sil with some insane-sounding chuckles.

Sil was a friend of Shapiro's, "not that we have the same line, if Sil has a line, but what he's into's important—cultural radicalism. I mean, it's part of the movement. I concede there's no discipline to it. It's sort of a running theatrical critique, but it has a place. You have to be crazy to do it, but Sil's crazy."

Shapiro went to classes and did the work and carried a 4.8 grade-point average, all the while denouncing the University's scoring system, its whole pedagogy as "obedience training, a parody of anything I'd call education, but a serviceable system for producing the personnel they need for the public and private bureaucracies."

"You're right, but don't neglect your marks," his father, the CPA, would say. "You never know what's going to happen."

Shapiro didn't neglect his marks. He could argue against the University's system, but he couldn't bear being out of it. He thought it was quite possible he'd finish his youth in the penitentiary for defying the war and the draft, but he knew he wanted to go to jail a doctor of philosophy.

Sil was different. He looked different. Tall and ugly with jerky, basketball player's movements. Sometime in the last few years he'd matriculated as a freshman; maybe he was still a student in his own mind and maybe he wasn't. He lived in the University neighborhood and acted as though his family was still paying tuition. There were a lot of people like him, so many that the student government types who ran the Union complained about "non-students who don't pay fees using our facilities." They singled out Sil as a conspicuous example.

"It's my University, too," Sil would say without explaining. Sil didn't explain things. He seldom even had conversations. With people he appeared to take seriously, like Shapiro, he would be quiet for long periods, working on what he called his contraptions, "machines that make nothing, man, that's a contraption. I make better contraptions than General Motors." He made all kinds: machines that repeated themselves in fluid, restful motions; eccentric machines that seemed mechanically impossible because their parts appeared to operate without pattern or sequence; funny machines that began by looking like efficient stainless steel parts milled to marvelous tolerances and finished by making weird, crackpot noises.

Some of Sil's contraptions were small and manually operated. These he would sometimes take out of his pocket and wordlessly display to a stranger. He also had very large contraptions, variously powered by electricity, gasoline, water, or wind. When he finished building one, he'd start it going and leave it somewhere. Several monstrous, quacking, mocking contraptions had been left in the Student Union. Another had been left in the hall outside the president's office suite. Hungerford's secretary thought it was a bomb and called the police, who declared it strange but probably not dangerous. An assistant curator from the DuPont Museum was summoned. He pronounced it a work of art and with four professional movers managed after two days of struggle to get it out of Fletcher Hall, across the Square and into the Museum, where it is still on exhibit, snarling, bopping, snapping, and surprising in random mechanical gesture. A plaque in front of it reads: ANONYMOUS. PROBABLY LATE TWENTIETH-CENTURY AMERICAN.

Sil also made masks, beautifully crafted, repulsively ugly *papier-mâché* personae. "They're states of mind, emotions, that's what they are," he would say. These he kept, or, if he gave them away, nobody knew about it. He had a large collection of them in the panel truck which he owned and appeared to live in when he wasn't camping in somebody else's place or with the girl who called herself Monique.

She was so unlike French perfume that Shapiro couldn't believe it was her real name. Sil called her Slob Child, or, for a variant, Slob Chick. She was uglier than he and less accomplished. There was nothing she seemed able to do, not cook, not sew, not keep herself clean. She talked foolishness and was always being fired from jobs that asked no more than punctuality. Monique, the Slob Child, and Sil were always in each other's company. She was tolerated because she went with him.

Shapiro would shrug his shoulders and say of Sil, "We relate to each other by talking in verbal ideograms. It's funny, but it's communication." It was more than Sil offered people outside his circle. Not that he was silent or inarticulate. Occasionally he was, but that was when he was playing the role of offensive gawker. In one-to-one encounters his preferred method of blocking communication was by sensing what people thought of him and playing the part back. He had the words to be a hippy, an alienated youth, a schizophrenic, a goon, a ghoul, or a cretin, but he refused to labor to make himself understood, to correct people's misjudgments of him—possibly because he was arrogant or hateful or too busy with what he actually was, or because he was being instructive, a sort of human contraption.

The consequence of his behavior was to give people who could stand being close to him the impression that he had no antecedents, that he'd come from nowhere, grown up in no place, a classless, raceless event. His way of living reinforced this picture. He slept in his panel truck, or with Monique, or in his bedroll in somebody's garage or workshop or studio. He owned no tools of his own, so he had to use other people's to make his masks and contraptions from materials which Shapiro assumed he stole. He had no money to buy, but nobody came to arrest him.

"D'you believe Martin Luther King was a radical?" Sil asked Shapiro shortly after the Mungo business.

"No, I wouldn't say that, but he's got to be looked at as part of the process of politicization of black people. He couldn't conceive of overthrowing the system, but he did believe in resisting it. He shocked people's consciences, not in a very good way. I mean, his methods didn't lead to questioning from a radical point of—"

"Yeah," said Sil, "he shocked people. I want people shocked into the idea that they're living in a community of latent maniacs. I am going to build the E. J. Cornford Perpetual Expiatory Capability Contraption and Death Machine."

The Cornford Expiatory Contraption was erected on a special platform below the Minerva early one morning. Until noon it was covered with canvas bearing a sign with its name and an announcement that it would shortly do its work of mechanical atonement. Sil had costumed himself as a hangman and put a mask of horror over his hooded face. His two assistants were outfitted the same way, but with masks signifying Pain and Misery.

The skit was a mime, but realistically done. Monique had contributed the eleven cats who lived in her apartment. Other friends had come bringing their pets, including five or six dogs and a number of hamsters, whose lineage could be traced to one of the University's labs, as could the rhesus monkey's. The pigeons had been trapped in a municipal park, the black snake and raccoon were never explained any more than the owl. Sil had gone to a lot of trouble to get the owl.

A black kid, a member of the Student Afro Association, threatened to hit Big Shoulders if he got violent again when Sil turned the contraption on and people could see the blades and choppers. "Let it be, let it be," the black whispered, two cocked fists straight up near his shoulders.

The campus cops came running, but it was a big crowd and they were men well into middle age whose true functions were to report fires and turn the keys in their nightwatchmen's clocks. They backed off. In any case, the crowd was too big for them to do much with—four or five hundred unpredictable people.

For the most part they were nauseated as Sil threw the first cat in the contraption which appeared to skin it alive. As the next and the next and the next cat and the first of the hamsters were thrown in and drops of red dripped from the bottom of the box, a section of the crowd moved forward to stop it, but they were intimidated by Pain, Misery, and several other members of the Student Afro Association who, without saying anything, backed the crowd off.

Red was flowing freely from the E. J. Cornford Expiatory Capability Contraption and Death Machine, and the watching crowd below and on the sides of the high steps where the Minerva stood had grown large with quiet, bug-eyed people, couples holding hands, infuriated assistant deans, and stupefied faculty members.

The last animal to go in was the owl, who brought a groan and murmuring of nooooo. When the owl had been completely devoured, Sil kicked a switch at the base of the contraption. The animals, terrified but unhurt, came flying, scuttering, screeching, barking, and squealing out of the machine at the crowd which broke, shouting in fear, and ran back ten or fifteen feet before it collected itself and stopped. Pain and Misery ran off. The skit was over. The DuPont Museum had another statue if it cared to come across the Square and pick it up.

Within three days All University Regulation XXVII was published. It prohibited any form of demonstration, theatricale, speech, song, or music by everyone except registered students, faculty, teaching assistants, or other University employees, without prior approval from one of the more important deans.

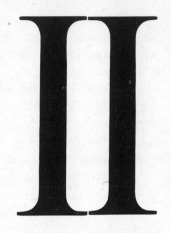

HIS ENTRY in *Who's Who* read:

McVey, A.A. b. 1915, m. Elizabeth Bayer Spring 1941, children, Arlene 1943, A.A. Jr. 1945, Sarah Elizabeth 1949. AB Beloit College, MA, PhD (economics) University of Wisconsin, LLB Harvard; member of Massachusetts and U.S. Supreme Court bar; Assistant Chief Counsel, Monopoly Subcommittee, U.S. Senate, 1938–40; Assistant Professor of Economics, University of Chicago, 1940–41; major, United States Army, 1942–45; Associate Professor of Economics, Columbia University, 1945–48; Assistant Attorney General of the U.S. (Anti-Trust Division), 1949–51; Professor of Government, Woodrow Wilson School, Princeton University, 1952–61; Wharton Lecturer on Economics and Law, Yale University, 1955; Visiting Professor, Université de Paris, 1959; Special Assistant to the President, 1961–64; Albert

Lyon Thompson Professor of Economics at the University, 1964–68; Chancellor of the University, 1969–; Publications: "Monopoly Capital and Political Power," 1941; "Oligopoly and the Business Cycle," 1947; "Econometrics," 1953; "Social Pluralism—Midway in the American Century," 1958; "Progress with Poverty," 1962; numerous articles. Member of the National Academy of Science, American Economic Association, Council of Economic Advisers, National Board of the American Civil Liberties Union, American Association of University Professors, President's Committee on Law and Justice, executive committee of Americans for Democratic Action.

Vernon Yaldell had two pieces of reading matter on his desk. One was a book containing the charters of the medieval kings of England, out of which he hoped to fish an aside for his doctoral dissertation, three and a half doleful years in the writing. In front of him, taking up the time and psychic energy he felt he owed the Angevins, was today's copy of the *Daily Review* on whose first page All University Regulation XXVII was printed in bold-face type. Although he had read it four times, he continued to look at it as he talked to Blackie McTavish, his boss in the hierarchy of deans. McTavish was *the* Associate Dean of Students, while Yaldell was one of a great many assistant deans. Functionally, Yaldell was important because his office was in the Student Union where he operated as a kind of forward observation post. He was the dean most in contact with the fifteen thousand undergraduates. Whenever a chill of apprehension hit middle-echelon management at the University, somebody jangled Yaldell's telephone for intelligence.

"It's too early to tell what's going on in the fo'csle, Blackie. The crew ain't gonna like it. . . . Well, what do I think? I told you, I haven't talked to anybody yet. . . . Oh no, I think if I did that I'd just give people ideas. . . . Yeah, yeah, I know it would help to have a reading before the meeting with A.A., but if I turn up downstairs in the Owl Cove just, ha ha, casually asking people, ha ha, what they, ha ha, think of Regulation XXVII, I'm not going to learn anything we don't know. Besides, I don't want to talk to anybody about it because I don't know what the hell it means. God, from the way it reads, it sounds like we're supposed to call the campus cops if we catch Hungerford's mother humming to herself. I think it's unenforceable, Blackie. . . . Well, I hope A.A. does have a 'workable interpretation' for us this afternoon. . . . Yeah, well, I'd like to say something at that meeting. . . . Well, yes, I know I'm free to, but I want to say something in plain deck language, even if it bruises some people's feelings. . . . Okay, okay, Blackie, I'm not feeling I'm under any constraints, I just mention it to you in advance. What I want to say is that A.A. had better stop going out of town, because every time he does, Hungerford pulls something like this. . . . Well, I know A.A.'s going to say he stands behind XXVII. What else can he say? But you and I both know he was out of town. I'm not even sure XXVII is legal. Doesn't the Academic Senate have to ratify it at least? . . . Hell, you know I don't care if it's legal, but we're the ones who have to live with this stuff. This is the second time we've had something like this in two weeks. Hungerford was lucky with the Mungo business. And that's another example of his pulling something when A.A. goes away for the weekend. He's not going to be so lucky all the time. It's all too nerve wracking. I don't know whether Hungerford and some of those other people marooned up there in Fletcher Hall realize it, but last year was rough. . . . Yeah, well, rough on you and me. I got almost nothing done on my dissertation.

"Well, Blackie, that's nice of you to say that. I appreciate it, but I'm still living to get that thing done so I can get out of here. I've had it with multiversities. Look, I enjoy working with undergraduates. I like being a dean, even a dean third-class, but I want to go to a small school. Don't you sometimes feel we're like officers on a ship with a crew that may mutiny? Every time anything happens you call up, the others call you . . . 'What's going on in the fo'csle? What're the men saying?' And meanwhile there are the passengers. . . . We're the passengers. The faculty are dumping on us."

Several hours later Blackie called back to say that McVey was busy. There would be no meeting with the deans and sub-deans, but Fletcher Hall would provide guidance in the form of a memorandum, which Blackie was sending over directly. Call back if there're any questions. Yaldell decided against telling Blackie what he was now convinced of, that All University Regulation XXVII would be tested.

Regulation XXVII is clarificatory. It spells out in more concrete language what already is implicit in paragraph IX of the University Statutes and in All University Regulation XI, Yaldell read and then said aloud, "It's like the Vatican. We never add anything new, never change anything old. We legislate by making distinctions." *The University remains an institution committed to the free marketplace of ideas, and nothing in Regulation XXVII should be construed to mean prior constraint or censorship. Its purpose is to protect the campus as a place where members of the University community (staff and students) can continue to enjoy free speech over the widest spectrum of topics and to prevent the University from becoming a staging area or recruiting ground for political and social groupings. It should be made clear to all that the regulation in no way prohibits non-University people from speaking on the campus as long as they are invited guests of either*

*faculty or officially approved student organizations and per-
mission for their appearance is secured beforehand. Many
other universities have similar regulations. As with all rules
this one should be enforced with good judgment, moderation,
and even leniency. Its sole purpose is to defend this campus
against extremist elements whose objectives are not educational
but are the seizure of institutions of higher learning for ideological and partisan purposes.*

Yaldell called Blackie to tell him he'd read the memo
and was locking it up. "How'd you like to read that in the
Daily Review? Whoever wrote it ought to enforce it. Does
it mean we have to report every off-campus speaker who
says *anything* at *any* meeting? And if it doesn't, then which
speakers are we supposed to report? The ones we disagree
with?" And on that note he said goodbye to Blackie, gave
in to a brief reflection that he might have the wrong dissertation topic, and wandered downstairs to the Owl Cove.

He heard nothing but music from the juke box, saw
nothing but the mastication of hamburgers and french fries.
The coming trouble wasn't discernible here. These were
the kinds of students it was a pleasure to work with, putting
out yearbooks and literary anthologies, doing plays, worrying about the idea of absolutes in Plato or how they could
personally contribute to the betterment of man, or about part-
time jobs, late papers, and switching majors. Even Shapiro
was a kid Yaldell could identify with, a nice cerebral
radical who was interesting to debate.

Shapiro had done a lot of head scratching and decided
that an action would get some support from the "unpoliti-
cized student underclass." Regulation XXVII had to be
tested, but he wasn't a person to walk in and just bring it

up at the SDS chapter meeting. He gentled people along, letting meetings drift, and acted more like a member than a chairman.

"There's a little paragraph from Kierkegaard I'd like to read and then throw the meeting open," Shapiro said.

"Shapiro, what the hell are you? A rabbi? Why do we have to have this Talmudic bullshit," Roger Elias, the teaching assistant in math, began shouting.

"What I was going to read is directly to the point, and it's not very long," Shapiro replied. He was used to Roger.

"A revolution isn't a delicatessen. You're a victim of Jewish traditionalism. Always we gotta have a little lesson of wisdom to meditate over. I want to act."

"I withdraw the Kierkegaard. Brother Elias wants to act."

That produced a complaint of nooos and a fumbling around until several people said they objected and wanted to hear the Kierkegaard. Shapiro was trusted. Roger wasn't. What came out of Roger's mouth was too frightening, too aggressive, too egocentric, and sometimes so fascinating it induced suspicion.

" 'Everyone knows a great deal, we all know which way we ought to go, but nobody is willing to move,' " Shapiro read aloud. " 'If at least someone were to overcome the reflection within him and happened to act, then immediately thousands of reflections would form an outward obstacle. Only a proposal to reconsider a plan is greeted with enthusiasm; act is met with indolence.' "

"Do it! Do it! Do it!" Roger began chanting. Five or six people came in with him. Shapiro waited until they'd subsided before he tried speaking: "Roger, we're going to do it, but some of us would like to know what we're going to do. It's a serious business that could affect our lives, and we ought to be aware of everything it means so that thousands of reflections don't form an outward obstacle when we get out of here. I've been to too many meetings where a hundred people agree on an action and eleven turn up for it the next morning.

"There're several possibilities for action. A petition is already being circulated—"

Roger was interrupting and shouting again, "Shapiro, you better get your shit together. A petition? For a guy who thinks he's such a sharp radical thinker, you sound like Hubert Humphrey."

"Will you let me finish?" Shapiro came close to shouting back. "I was enumerating what was going on already and what we might do, okay? If you want to know what *I* think, I think we should test them as soon as possible. Have a rally, not ask permission and invite people like A. J. Muste or Norman Thomas or I. F. Stone."

"I don't. I don't want a test. I want a challenge. I want a declaration of war. I want another Pentagon here. I want people like Jerry Rubin to say dirty words and take off their clothes. I want to put 'em up tight, that's what I want. I'm not interested in busting Regulation XXVII. I want to bust it and the twenty-six that come before it. Break open the whole place," Roger replied.

Shapiro scratched his hair and said, "No, you can't do it that way. The E. J. Cornford Machine proved that. Most of that crowd was against us. We've got to have a very dignified kind of rally to win the faculty on our side. You're not going to mobilize the faculty to defend somebody who takes his pants off in public. Remember, there's no radical constituency here."

"There was no radical constituency at Berkeley before Berkeley or at Columbia before there was a Columbia. You make radicals by radical action."

"You don't make radicals by turning people off. They're not going to accept leadership from a bunch of people they consider irresponsible weirdos. Roger, you're misreading

Columbia and Berkeley. It wasn't the nutty, ego-tripping performances of a few wild individuals that did it. It was sound, carefully planned tactics which ultimately forced the administration to act according to its true social role," Shapiro said in tones almost pedagogical.

"And I'm telling you, the soundest tactics, Shapiro, are to freak out their minds. I mean the minds of the Administration. They can always handle you, for Christ sake. You're one of them."

"Look, Roger, I'm not going to get involved in one of those I'm-more-radical-than-you contests, but I just wish you'd cut out attacking me all the time because I'm Jewish, because I'm straight, because I try to figure out what I'm doing before I do it. Just cut it out, will you?"

"I won't cut it out because it's screwing up the revolution. You think like a Jew, a Jewish intellectual. You've got the same mind-set the administration has. They can always deal with you. You're a proceduralist, a formalist, due process. They've got you by the brain, Shapiro."

"Well, what do you suggest we do?"

"You're going to die a full professor, reading their books, going by their rules, and you'll never beat them because you think like them. There's only one way they can be beaten, that's making them use their own strength against themselves. They must be enticed to commit atrocities, baited and lured."

"Roger, *I* know that."

"Yeah, you know it and *they* know it, too. What do you think—they haven't learned anything? If you know, if you of all people know it, *they* know. That's your chief tactical value to the revolution around here. Whenever I want to know what A. A. McVey is thinking, I talk to you, but what you *don't* know and they don't know and can't defend against is fighting off the terrain of their experience. The E. J. Cornford Expiatory Capability Contraption and Death

Machine. *That* they don't know how to contend with, so they react with Regulation XXVII. Goddamn it, Shapiro, learn, learn from what's happened already, and no more bullshit about some legalistic test."

The outcome was the letter, mimeographed and tacked on the outer doors of every building except Fletcher Hall, where, out of perversity or a misplaced sense of etiquette, a typewritten and signed original was fixed:

GREETINGS UNCLE HUNGERFORD:
"Up against the wall, motherfucker, this is a stickup." Those are the words Mark Rudd used at Columbia to announce the coming of the revolution there.

Now we use the same words here.

People who get revolted against never understand why. You probably can't understand why the students of this university would want to call you dirty names and chase you out of here as though you were no better than a losing football coach. You are worse than a losing football coach. You are even worse than a winning coach. But why do we think so poorly of you, Uncle Hungerford?

First, you are a racist.

For the twenty years you've run this knowledge factory, you've been stealing the land and the houses of the black community that surrounds us. In the name of expansion, progress, and the University's great contributions to mankind, you've called on the poor blacks to sacrifice their homes. Uncle Hungerford, what have you ever sacrificed for this university?

Second, you sacrificed the blacks to a racist institution, to what would be an ivy-covered munitions factory if the plutocrats on the University's board of trustees hadn't fouled this city's air so badly ivy won't grow. Large amounts of the University's endowment are invested in Rhodesian mining stocks, South African industries, and public utilities in Alabama and Mississippi. Wherever black men slave for white man's profit, this university gets its cut.

Third, you've sacrificed the blacks for the University and you've sacrificed the University to war. There is no method of inflicting injury and death that is too horrible for this University not to invent, perfect, and take money for.

We are on to you, Uncle Hungerford. The students, much of the faculty, the blacks, even the white middle class is on to you and can see that Regulation XXVII was thought up to prevent us from mounting any kind of effective political action on this campus. It's the old academic-freedom confidence game. We can say anything we want, just so long as you manipulate things so our words are harmless.

You have robbed us of the political rights we would automatically have if we were not students. You can do this because students are the new niggers of our society. We are absolutely powerless. You have robbed us of our political rights because you say you want to keep this holy shrine of knowledge and scholarship politically neutral, because you don't want any outside groups coming in here recruiting us. You should be sick to puking with your own lies. No outside groups except Dow Chemical, the Army, the Navy, the Marines, IBM, CIA, you name it—any organization from the militocracy can come here and recruit all they want. Why, Uncle Hungerford, you even supply them with rooms, phones, and secretarial services. The only groups barred from recruiting are pacifist or socialist.

This is the neutral haven of scholars—fifty-one per cent financed by war research—that Regulation XXVII wants to keep pure and protected from off-campus agitators. It won't work, Uncle Hungerford. There are inside agitators, too—they used to be called students—and they are going to stuff Regulation XXVII down your throat two days from now, when we have an unauthorized rally featuring off-campus speakers talking to the academic field hands without your permission.

If the rising spirit of revolutionary anarchy, as I guess

you probably call it, baffles and mystifies you, come to the rally and we'll try to explain why this is a stickup, and why we're going to put you up against the wall, motherfucker.

Sincerely yours,
ROGER ELIAS

There was no reaction. Liberal institutions don't react to words, even when they are posted in violation of the rule that requires them to carry a seal from the Dean of Students' office before they may be affixed to a bulletin board, a wall, or a door. The University was impervious to words, all words in any arrangement. The marketplace of ideas doesn't insist the merchandise be examined or bought. Exhibition is enough.

"That's why I believe in violence," Shapiro used to say. "Violence is a way of communicating with 'them.' 'They' won't listen to words which aren't backed up by force. If you talk without physically threatening them, they say to themselves, 'Oh, he's talking words, and words are symbols that stand for things which these kids aren't old enough to understand or rich enough to own.' "

Roger was probably counting on the word 'motherfucker' to draw a reaction, "but I doubt it," Shapiro had argued with Roger. "Obscenity bugs them, but they don't try to get anybody on it. Spoils their liberal image of themselves. Besides, to get you they'd have to accuse you of calling them motherfuckers, and you know they're not going to use that word in public. Anyway, they're not going to make martyrs, not free-speech martyrs. Hungerford might try it. He's got the makings of an obliging reactionary, but McVey won't let him. He's the most treacherous kind of liberal. I can just imagine McVey steering Hungerford away from doing anything. I can almost hear the conversation."

After the letter had been posted on the doors, Fletcher Hall appeared especially institutional, chartered, and endowed. And the word was made stone. It was the ancient regime before there was a gap to look back at the ancient regime from and coin the expression. Solidity. It was there in limitless permanence, but nothing issued out of it.

Shapiro could imagine the scene inside Fletcher with an acuity Hungerford couldn't apply reciprocally to Shapiro. They had never met; each thought of the other as a class. But Shapiro had one advantage: he'd made the effort to consider Hungerford as a specific representative of his class with his own individualizing traits. He had read about Hungerford, heard his convocation speeches, researched him, gone with the undergraduate throng to the yearly reception at the president's house, stood by the Minerva and looked into the windows he supposed were Hungerford's offices.

"Let's not make martyrs," Shapiro could imagine McVey, the civil libertarian and sophisticate, saying.

"Martyrs make themselves. When somebody wants to be a martyr, sooner or later you have to oblige him," Hungerford might respond. Shapiro always thought of Hungerford as blunt, tending toward brutal, a conservator without apology. It was McVey who was despised. "Destroy their eggs. Pour kerosene on the larvae. Get them in ova," Hungerford might argue, or, because he had a pompous streak in him, he might say, "I will not permit dirty words to be scratched all over the walls of the University. Free speech is one thing, but this is another. The line has to be drawn, and you needn't worry about who will have the public sympathy on campus and off. I've been here longer than you, McVey. This isn't Berkeley, you know."

Hungerford couldn't imagine Shapiro with such precision. He probably hadn't heard his name. He may not even have read the letter until much later, after the crisis had begun and was recognizable to all.

To Fletcher Hall the revolutionary radicals were unresolved

images of hirsute unhealthiness, known mainly through articles in liberal magazines which said, No, no, it isn't paranoia, there are a certain number of young people who do meet to plan the campus takeover. They are, the magazines declared, romantic Marxists—wild, alienated ones with identity crises that cause them to emulate Che Guevara. Not very rich material with which to realize the conversations of the youthful enemy.

The actors thought reality lay in the worthless secrets and unrecorded conversations; conspiracy, the non-evidential, what was deduced and surmised, must explain the public acts. For them it was a time when public acts weren't plausible, when famous men were murdered in front of the television cameras, their deaths replayed over and over again in the fantastic accuracy of fact without intelligibility.

In actuality, all the secrets and unrecorded conversations at the University were worthless. Everything that happened was done in public in conformance with tactics and models of thought, speech, and action which had become commonplace in the land. Deception was impossible. Everyone knew what everyone else was up to, how all sides would react, what moves and countermoves would be made, the fact that there could be no surprises, nothing unforeseen—this undisguised constant made the whole sequence of events unthinkable. It did not work that way. History taught none of the principals at the University what to avoid. What it did was to supply the ground rules, the givens for everybody to adhere to.

The Minerva had one hand above her head pointing slightly forward toward heaven and the other coming out of her robes, palm outward, in a receptive position. Sil, who wore a mask depicting some character out of oriental demonology, sat on Minerva's palm. It put him above and behind the speakers standing at the base of the statue and allowed him to shoot the crowd with a movie camera as it looked up from the steps of the Square to listen. The elongated demon on Minerva's palm, pointing his machine at them, caused no special comment. In the last few years, people at the University had gotten used to freakish behavior and outlandish costume. Only Yaldell was concerned with Sil.

"Should I get *his* name too?" the assistant dean asked his boss, Blackie McTavish, whom he was standing next to. "He doesn't look like he's sponsoring the meeting."

"Just the leaders, Vern," McTavish answered, folding his arms across his chest and tilting his chin skyward as a man might do if he wanted to look as though he had no part in anything that was going on.

"Oh, hell," said Yaldell, and began moving through the five hundred or so people who composed the audience toward the speakers and the amplifying equipment. There he found Roger Elias, who seemed to be in charge of the meeting.

"My name is Dean Yaldell and I'm going to have to ask you to—"

"Get lost."

"I said, my name is Dean Yaldell and I'm here to inform you that—"

"Get lost."

The student on the microphone at that moment was there for the purpose of introducing the professor from the history department who was going to introduce Norman Thomas. He recognized Yaldell in his peripheral vision and, guessing what was up, boomed into the loudspeaker, "It looks like we're having a little confrontation here. If I'm not mistaken, that's Vernon Yaldell from the Dean of Students' office. Mr. Yaldell, if you have anything to say, you can say it right here. We don't run our meetings the way you run your university. We'd be happy to hear anything you have to say."

Laughter from the steps and a refocusing of the camera

lens by the oriental devil, while Yaldell looked at the speaker and then back at Roger Elias, whom he started to address for a third time. But Roger was gone from him. He had taken the mike and, half talking to the audience and half to Yaldell, was saying, "Mr. Yaldell is new to our movement, so I should tell him that we don't believe in little private conversations or gentlemen's agreements. If you want to tell me anything, just come up here and tell it to everybody and then we'll see what everybody decides."

Blackie McTavish lowered the point of his nose. Yaldell looked indecisive and then took a backward step.

"Whatever the administration had on its mind couldn't be very important. I see Mr. Yaldell is leaving. If you should change your mind, you're always welcome to talk at our meetings."

Then Yaldell appeared to change his mind. He came forward and up to Roger, who smiled and offered him the mike.

"I don't want that," he said, so Roger held it in front of Yaldell's mouth. Yaldell brushed it away. Roger reasserted the mike and Yaldell put a hand over it. A rising hubbub from the crowd, but whether it was sympathy, protest, laughter, or just excitement was impossible to tell.

"This meeting is a violation of Regulation XXVII," Yaldell said, but as he did, Roger for a second time pushed the mike forward so Yaldell's next words were audible to all. "In as much as you are having off-campus speakers, I must ask you to stop and conform to the rules and regulations of the University."

"Not you, not you!" Roger cried out. "Not you, but us! We're the University. We, the students and the faculty. We will obey the rules we make for ourselves, and not the rules the Administration decides to put on us by fiat." He was getting encouragement from the crowd. "And the last rule in the world we will accept is a gag on free speech. We don't recognize your rules."

"How did I get into this?" Yaldell said, and the crowd

laughed while he paused and seemed to take stock of his position. At the back of the crowd, Blackie McTavish was making all kinds of signs, none of which were comprehensible. "Look, this regulation isn't a gag on free speech. Every society, every community has rules so that it can function. Traffic laws aren't passed to limit your personal liberty, your freedom of movement, but to see that everybody gets where he wants to go without being killed. Well, the same thing's true here."

Roger did a half-turn away from Yaldell, so that he could face the crowd head on, as he said, "The dean here is a gullible, complacent fathead. He has to be if he believes what he's just said. Or he's a sell-out."

"Sell-out! Sell-out!" the people in front of the crowd began chanting, but stopped when Yaldell started to make his reply. Roger again put the microphone in front of Yaldell's mouth.

"Would you please take that away," Yaldell said, anger evident in a certain breathiness about his speech.

"No."

"You're being discourteous."

A few people in the crowd laughed, but most waited as Roger retorted that decorum would have to give way in a contest for First Amendment rights, and added, "You shits in the Administration can't put manners above morals. Probity comes before propriety. I'll be goddamned if I'm rude as long as I'm right. We're right, got that, motherfucker?"

"I'll have to take your name and that of the other people who've sponsored this meeting," Yaldell said. His voice was low and uneven.

"You goddamn well know my name. I know you have a file on me. We're not going to play these games with you any more. They're simply a form of intimidation."

"I don't know your name. We don't keep files—not in the sense you mean it—on our students."

"Like hell you don't."

"I will have to ask you for your student identification card."

"Why don't you go fuck yourself?"

"On the back of the card, it says it must be shown when asked for by an officer of the University. I'm an officer and I'm asking to see your card."

Some boos came up out of the crowd toward the two of them facing each other across the mike.

"Refusal to show your student ID is an infraction of the rules," Yaldell said amid the lowing and booing. It was still only a minority of the crowd which was making the noise, and their noise wasn't angry as much as it seemed to be expressing the idea of, "Oh, you've got to be kidding. Cut the crap." Yaldell lost the huffy temper in his tone. McTavish had his arms crossed and was staring at Roger. "Will you please show me your ID?"

"It's a helluva system, isn't it?" Roger asked, and his amplified voice echoed off the pompous buildings that delineated the limits of the Square. "ISN'T IT? ISN'T IT? isn't it? They expect you to conform to their bureaucratic rigmarole to help them cut off your head. It's the same mentality that wants to make sausages from hogs of uniform size. I've told you once, Yaldell—see, I know *your* name—go fuck yourself, FUCK YOURSELF—yourself—yourself."

While Roger and Yaldell were having at it, Ellie Rector moved up the steps to the front of the crowd. She had both arms wrapped around school books which she pressed to her chest. Although she had spent the better part of three years as an undergraduate, the original notes, taken by the admission's office counselor, were still in her student file, along with all her subsequent grades, routine memos from the student health office and the bursar, stray correspondence, and other minutiae that nobody would have call to read. None of it, save only the first set of notes, would be useful in delineating a coeducational human with a grade-point average on the upper part of the curve:

Ellie is a very attractive girl, something of a late bloomer, I suspect. She may be quite outstanding physically in a couple more years. She has good, suburban high school manners, and is well poised as long as the conversation stays within a range of topic and opinions she is used to and expects from the mouth of a university representative. Surprise her and she reverts to being a teen-ager. In other words, I don't think there's much creativity or flexibility there. She's a good girl who wants to know what you want of her so she can do it.

Despite the fact that her College Boards are fairly high, I'm not satisfied she's actually so smart as she's good at regurgitating whatever it is that older people tell her. She's a cheerful thing, quite pleasant, but she gives the impression of being rehearsed rather than polished. In the interview she talked a lot about maturity—her word—and balance. She kept saying she didn't like going overboard. This is certainly reflected in her grades, which are almost the same in every subject. She told me in high school she'd gone out for one extracurricular activity of "each kind—intellectual, social, and athletic," so she wouldn't be "too far one way." So she was a cheer leader, a member of the French Club and the tennis team.

If she weren't so sweet, I'd suspect her of being calculating, but I don't think she is. She says she might want to join a sorority, but she isn't sure. Her reason for making the University her first choice is that her father got his Master's degree in business administration here. He's an executive of a chemical company, so Ellie won't be needing financial assistance.

I recommend we take her in the hope that four years here can prick her into asking a few questions and perhaps even once in her life striking out on her own. We'll probably fail, in which case we'll have supplied the captain of the basketball team with a pretty, reasonably literate nincompoop for a wife.

As she stood at the top of the stairs, Ellie looked like the unripened teen-ager described in the files. There was a symmetrical prettiness in her face but still nothing to read, no feature to fix on and say it showed character.

"Yourself, yourself, yourself," was still echoing back and forth off the ornate cement and stone when Yaldell turned to try to get the names of some of the other principals. Before he did, he came up against Ellie. She had separated herself from the crowd and come the rest of the way. "If you'll please hold my books, Mr. Yaldell, I'll get my card out of my purse and you can take my name as one of the sponsors of the meeting."

"You?" Yaldell said, holding up his hands for the books which she pushed on him.

"Yes, me. I go to the University, too," she said, and the crowd stood puzzled, and then someone laughed and then five or six others came up to give their names, and then five or six more and then ten, and then thirty, then more and more, and then the history professor who was to introduce Norman Thomas, and then Norman Thomas. The demon on the outstretching palm of Minerva got it all on film.

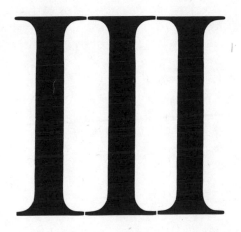

III

"The purpose of Regulation XXVII is to prevent outside groups from using this institution for non-academic, non-educational objectives which have nothing to do with the true usages of a university. It was not meant to place any kind of limitation, censorship, or prior restraint on the expression of ideas. This being the case, I can't conceive that a meeting at which so distinguished a man as Norman Thomas is the major speaker could offend against Regulation XXVII. That isn't what the regulation was designed for."—Chancellor A. A. McVey, as quoted in an interview in the *Daily Review*

"The Administration has wisely, we think, not chosen the Norman Thomas meeting to test its new regulation. Any attempt to discipline students for inviting Norman Thomas to speak would create a national furor and would seriously

damage our reputation on other campuses. It would also prove that Roger Elias and the other people who organized the Thomas meeting were right and that Regulation XXVII was designed to be a gag and not simply a traffic rule as Dean Yaldell said. As a traffic regulation we support XXVII. Every community must live by rules, and in this time of controversy a system has to be worked out for making sure public meetings are orderly and that all groups have an equal chance to hold their meetings at the feet of Minerva. Therefore, we commend the Chancellor for the position he has taken, and doubly so because with more than two hundred having turned in their names, any attempt to punish them would risk creating a campus uproar. We don't think our University is any more likely to have an uproar than some other place. In fact, there's less danger of trouble here than on other campuses because of the good spirit, good communication, and generally solid relations among most students, faculty, and administration. Even so, it's a jittery, tense year on campus and in the ghetto, a year when people of good will who are dedicated to the whole community should not push things to the limit, even when they are technically right in their positions."—Editorial appearing in the same issue of the *Daily Review*

"No politically knowing person on this campus expects much from the Daily Review, *tied as it is to the School of Journalism with all its deals and connections with the establishment mass media. But even the liberal press, where I assume you J-School graduates hope to get a job, has fought for the right of free speech, sterile as that usually is. Only the student press, the "student nigger press" Roger Elias calls it, would say the test of being a person of good will is not enforcing your own rights.*

"Your acceptance of Yaldell's interpretation of XXVII as a 'traffic' regulation is incredible. Even if you find a way to overlook the fact that it was unilaterally promulgated on us

without consultation with the Academic Senate or that romper room known as the student government, and that it was created as a direct result of a meeting the Administration disapproved of, you should still be able to see it is no traffic regulation. It sets up no system for the orderly use of the Minerva steps for meetings. It just says we cannot have any meeting with an outside speaker if the Dean of Students does not want it.

"When are you 'dedicated' editors of 'good will' going to realize that not every older person in authority is your friend who is doing what's best for you? The tragedy of the situation on this campus is that they don't need to oppress us. We cannot give our rights away to them fast enough."—Ray Shapiro, University Chapter of SDS, Letter to the Editor of the *Daily Review*

The modern novelist and social scientist solve the problem of analyzing a complex event by saying that the sum of the subjective understandings of the participants can produce a holographic image of objective reality. This was the assumption on which the Verbal History Project was based. After the revolution, the Project was financed by the Ford Foundation, which gave several hundred thousand dollars to tape record as many recollections of what happened as possible. These were eventually published in several large volumes which make fascinating, if confused, reading.

Relevant sections from Vernon Yaldell's transcript from the Verbal History Project:

YALDELL: You know, it's funny, but that day to the best of my recollection was the first and only time I ever had a conversation with Elias. Afterward, I saw him around a lot, and I may have said a few words to him, but that was the only time we ever talked. I remember itching to give him a karate chop. I was in the Green Berets in Vietnam. I've been trained to give karate chops. Of course, that's funny, too, because in many ways I agree with him about the war. I don't know how I felt about the war before I got to Nam, but after I was there for a while it occurred to me that the only way I could go on fighting and not become a pathological killer was to oppose it. That may seem strange to you. Maybe it makes me sound like the good German. I didn't think it out too clearly. I certainly was never one of those who said to myself, I should go over there and fight so I could establish my credentials. That's too cold-blooded. But I believed in working within the system. And you can say—I've said it myself sometimes—that working within the system makes you an accomplice to . . . death. I almost said murder. Well, I guess it is in a way. You see an old person or a child killed—I don't care by whom, our side, their side—it's murder. It's terrible. I've never pretended it wasn't, but the people who work outside the system can't stop the killing. What have their tactics done? They've spread the fighting. Christ Almighty, they've brought it to this University, right on the Square itself.

I guess I'm getting off the topic, wasting the Ford Foundation's money, but it isn't off the topic. It would be wrong, basically wrong for people to get the idea that it was only the Roger Eliases who cared and felt deeply about the war or the ghetto or where we as people are going. It's just not true. The picture they've tried to paint of the administrators of this University as power manipulators, amoral careerists is wrong. I wept more tears over that war than Roger Elias. He only went to Hanoi on those left-wing junkets. I buried the dead, the Vietnamese and our own. I'm really getting off the track, aren't I.

INTERVIEWER: No, I don't think so.

YALDELL: Anyway, I also remember when I was up there with Elias almost bursting out laughing a couple of times. The whole thing struck me as funny somehow. I don't know. I was being so formal and proper and he was doing his crazy demagogy. Of course, that was the first time I'd ever heard America's number one dirty-mouth orator. I don't think he's funny now.

A lot of people have criticized me for taking the names. Thanks to that girl, Ellie Rector, I took a lot of names. I had writer's cramp. Actually, I was told to take names if I explained to them that it was an unauthorized meeting and they still continued it.

INTERVIEWER: Were there any plans to go further? I mean, to do more than take names, if they kept up with the meeting?

YALDELL: You mean like disconnecting the loudspeaker system or something like that? No. Absolutely not. We don't treat our students that way. We were following the usual disciplinary procedures, nothing special. I'd like to say here that, although I was instructed to take names and didn't like the idea of doing it because it put me on the spot, I didn't disagree with Blackie [McTavish]. I think what he did was quite proper. A lot of people said we were crazy to do it, but that's hindsight. You forget that Elias had papered the campus with an announcement that he was going to flaunt Regulation XXVII. I mean, he left us no maneuvering room. If he'd just had the meeting without saying he was having it for the single, specific purpose of violating XXVII, we could have overlooked it, and I'm sure we would have. Even before it started here, you have to remember we were aware of the potential. Every college and university administrator in America was. What would have happened if we'd turned our backs completely? This is a testing thing they were doing. Then they'd have Mungo and the Big Black Cats on campus and Rap Brown and Stokely Carmichael and they'd push and they'd push until they'd taken over the place—liberated it, as they say. Well, I'm no great lover of Martin Hungerford. In fact, this University would be better off if he'd retired five years ago, but he's a damn sight better at the job than Roger Elias would be. And that's the point. Look at the history of the schools that gave in at first and tried permissive tactics. Did they do any better than we?

If you want to criticize, then criticize Regulation XXVII—not the intent, but the way it was handled. It was done too quickly and it was too loosely written. Anyhow, by the time of the Norman Thomas meeting a confrontation was shaping up, though to be honest, I didn't really see it at the time. What happened next I had nothing to do with. After the meeting I gave Blackie the list of names and that was it. I was never consulted about the letters. The first rumor I got of it was from somebody on the *Daily Review*. I gave the names to Blackie McTavish and that's the last I heard of it till the thing blew up.

Martin Hungerford's testimony in the Verbal History Project runs to several hundred pages. If you believe his statements, he had nothing to do with the letters being sent out to the students, who became known as the Norman Thomas Five:

HUNGERFORD: I knew nothing about it. There's nothing irregular in that. This is a large institution, twenty-five thousand students, nearly eight thousand people on what we call the instructional staff, teachers, researchers, and so forth. Only in the most unusual case would the Dean of Students consult my office about a routine disciplinary case.

INTERVIEWER: Routine, Dr. Hungerford?

HUNGERFORD: Hardly routine now, after what's happened, but before the fact, yes, routine. May I say something here? There has been a lot of ah, well, comment about those letters, some of it rather hasty and, in my opinion, not carefully thought out. In the light of subsequent events, does it appear to you, would it appear to any dispassionate judge, that not sending those letters would have made a material difference in all the tragic, unhappy things that happened here? I think not. I think we were dealing with people whose behavior shows they could be taken at their own word, and their own word was and still is that they are revolutionaries.

Relevant excerpts from the transcript of A. A. McVey:

MC VEY: I was not contacted on the matter. The Dean of Students' office simply followed normal procedure in sending out the letters to the five asking them to come in for an interview. It should be stressed that at no point were the Norman Thomas Five ever disciplined for sponsoring that meeting. What actually happened has been twisted and distorted, the letters themselves exploited and made to seem what they were not. They were not punishment. They were not even notification of a disciplinary hearing, but a request that the five come in to discuss the situation, and out of that discussion Dean Pomfret or somebody in the Dean of Students' office would have made a determination on whether or not to hold a disciplinary hearing, which then would have been done in the normal way, through the Joint Student Administration Committee on Conduct and Behavior.

The point to be borne in mind is that Dean Pomfret conducted himself in accordance with due process, that the Norman Thomas Five were not disciplined, and I personally believe never would have been. The actions of the Administration were skillfully misrepresented by a small group of people on this campus. This group undoubtedly had help and advice from non-students, people who, you should bear in mind, are—I hate to sound melodramatic—but they are people who are trained in this sort of thing. I mean, they've schooled themselves in the techniques of agitation and inciting civil insurrections. A university is at a terrible disadvantage in dealing with such individuals. They use our own liberal laws, the open-ended structure of our institutions against us. Our mistake was that we are scholars. We've spent our lives in study, research, and teaching, not in learning the arts of social sabotage. As a result, we were plunged into a situation where we were inexperienced children faced with veteran, trained, cold-blooded opponents.

The last thing we wanted was an incident. We were worried there might be one, not because of any specific situation on this campus but because of the times. But I think I can say we were very sympathetic with the feelings of our students. I personally have had the deepest misgivings about the war, and Dr. Hungerford has made several speeches in which he said that its cost in lives, money, and maiming of the spirit is far more than even total victory could win back for us. We were not a reactionary institution. We are not reactionary men. I fought Joe McCarthy, the loyalty oaths, the witch hunts. For eight years I left government service because of that sort of thing. I didn't go to Washington, not once. I refused all consultancies.

At the time of the Norman Thomas meeting I was quoted as saying that I could not conceive of Regulation XXVII being applicable. It was never applied to the meeting for two reasons: it was not intended to be used to banish dissent from this campus, and we were very anxious to avoid doing anything that might touch off an incident. I think anyone who looks at our entire subsequent course of action can see throughout everything we maintained a flexible, lenient stance. We were afraid, especially after Berkeley and even more after Columbia, that something terrible might happen here or on any campus, and that was the one thing we didn't want more than anything else.

The Verbal History Project tapes include exhaustive interviews with Blackie McTavish, the Associate Dean of Students, and Pomfret, the Dean himself. They don't clarify much. Both men agree that Fletcher Hall was not informed before the fact. The two put even more stress on the routine nature of the letters which bore McTavish's signature. Both men also say they were sent out because, to use McTavish's words, "It was obvious that all the people who gave Vern [Yaldell] their names weren't in on it. The regulation only holds sponsors of unauthorized meetings responsible, and those five seemed to be the logical people to communicate with. . . . Eleanor Rector? . . . At the time it appeared Miss Rector was one of the leaders. I mean, we had nothing more to go on than her conduct that day. I have since been told that she wasn't—how do they say it—a 'political.' I don't believe that, considering how conspicuous she's been, but then how can you tell? That day it appeared to us, or to me, that there had been some prior planning and that she was part of it. I can't say I knew that to be a fact, but that's why the letters were sent out, so that I could talk to them and try to find out what was what. It might have been an instance of their interpreting Regulation XXVII differently from us and the whole matter might have been forgotten. Who knows?"

Myron Mirsky at the Faculty Club thought he knew. When he heard of the letters summoning the five students to McTavish's office, he announced, "I know what this is. It's a recapitulation of the last days of the Tsars. The worst possible kind of situation, a tottering autocracy. All the symptoms are there—the caprice, the flashes of arbitrary strength, misapplied, of course, the unaccountable inconsistencies of men with shaken confidence in their divine mandate to rule. We are witnessing the last days of the academic Romanovs. On Monday it's call a Duma, on Tuesday it's no Duma, Wednesday it's let's have a constitutional assembly, Thursday it's a Duma again, and on Friday arrest all the liberal leaders for treason! And the faculty, we're the bourgeoisie whom these madmen are going to destroy like they destroy themselves. No other explanation can fit the data. First they panic at Fletcher Hall and promulgate that ridiculous Regulation of theirs. That's the repressive cycle. Call the cossacks—ah, but they lose their nerve. Remember, great autocrats are never overthrown, they commit suicide when they no longer believe in themselves. So they let it out that XXVII will be leniently enforced. In other words, pay no attention to it. McVey announces Norman Thomas can always speak on this campus. But no, there's hysteria and bang! they're off in the other direction. They're digging their own graves and ours, too."

"Myron," his tablemate said, "You're being apocalyptical again. There's too much Old Testament in you, too much Isaiah."

"Yeah, Isaiah. 'Your hands are defiled with blood, and your fingers with iniquity; your lips have spoken lies, your tongue hath muttered perverseness. None calleth for justice, nor any pleadeth for truth. They trust in vanity and speak lies.' You know, my friend, I have moments when it occurs to me that we have a lot to answer for. You and I, we're clean. You don't do any dirty research, do you?"

"You mean classified? In astronomy? Certainly not."

"Well, I haven't either," Mirsky continued, "but do you really know what's going on around here? I don't. I hear there's a building right off this campus, owned, staffed, and operated by the University, where you need a security clearance to walk around. I don't know if it's true. What if we're working in a bomb factory?"

"I suppose to some extent we are."

"I'm depressed. Even with their pogroms the Romanovs provided security, order, and the excuse that to inquire outside your field of professional competence was pointless futility. But now, if we're watching the beginning of the end of the supreme autocrat, the Tsar of all the schools, colleges, and research centers, we're going to have to become morally functional again—if we haven't lost the knack."

"The sun will rise tomorrow. You admitted you were depressed."

"I'm also rushed. I've got five minutes to get over to listen to an idiot defend an inferior thesis which our committee will approve because none of us have the guts to tell this guy he wasted six years of our time and his money here."

"They have the same problem in my department," his tablemate sympathized. "They should let them in for a terminal Master's degree so they can leave and teach high school. I've suggested that for certain people the terminal Master's be a specific condition of admittance, but they want the students."

"They want the students and you know why. So they have an excuse to decorate the catalogue with useless courses and give the younger men in the department a lot of marginal folderol to teach while the oligarchs hog the major courses. We've had the same four men teaching theory in our department for almost fifteen years. More students, good or bad, is more fellowships, more research grants, more third-rate junk. And remember, we're a good university. Think what it's like in the bush leagues," Mirsky said.

"I do remember that as a graduate student I made some vows about what I'd do when I became a member of a tenured faculty somewhere," said his tablemate. "The chairman of my thesis committee never was on time for an appointment. I spent as much time waiting in the corridor as I did writing the thesis. I took an oath to myself that I'd never treat a graduate student like that."

"Did you make yourself any other promises about what you'd do?"

"Yes."

"Did you keep them?" Myron asked. "Don't answer. I didn't keep mine. Only the easy ones. Don't make your students wait. Make sure they're not starving to death if they're brilliant, practice euthanasia on the dumb ones, and make sure they all get relatively decent jobs."

The tablemate nodded. "I lost my zeal for reform after spending a couple of years in Europe. Compared to us, European professors are sadists."

"I don't have any excuses. They were throwing me just enough goodies so I could beguile myself into thinking I'm my own boss."

"Well, you are, Myron. Nobody tells you what to say in your classroom or what to write."

"So I'm sitting in my classroom being free and they're turning the rest of the place into a bomb factory. And you're no better. What were you doing? You had your eye to the viewing piece of your telescope, stargazing. The only reason I associate with you is to brag to my colleagues in the behavioral sciences that I lunch with an astronomer and we can communicate."

The tablemate laughed. "Myron, you should have been a stargazer. It would have given you a certain detachment ...perspective."

"Stargazing is a Wasp occupation. It substitutes patience for brilliance, and I'm a brilliant, excitable Jew. I could have been a mathematician, but never a stargazer. You sit there on your mountain top for months watching Mars going bumpity-bump, bump, bump, bump around her orbit and you think you've got something when you've measured one of the bumps."

"You had an opportunity to sit on the faculty committee that reviews all outside research contracts. You refused to sit on it, Myron."

"Maybe I should have. Maybe I was too ambitious or too busy to spare the time, but I'm on three committees already. I joined each of them thinking I could change something, but the final result is that I allow my name to be used to ratify a policy I don't believe in. Like now. Now I'm going off to vote for a dissertation I should vote against."

Mirsky took himself and what he was beginning to refer to as his "reviving conscience" slowly off to the thesis committee meeting. He had time to think, as always, through twenty years of university life. He could pause, consider, and postpone doing anything, postpone even considering what a man situated as he was at the University could do. Ellie Rector had no time. The letter gave a specific hour and day when she was to appear in the Dean of Students' office.

She'd had to read it several times before she got it through her head what it asked of her. She had never before in her life been in trouble, and it was hard for her to understand she was.

"Well, what did you think? After all, you gave your name and all. Didn't you think, Ellie, that something was going to happen to you?" her roommate asked.

"I guess not. Oh, I don't know," Ellie answered. Last year there had been a girl in the dorm who'd gotten pregnant, and Ellie remembered the same roommate asking the girl, "Well, what did you think? Didn't you think something was going to happen if you let him do it?"

"A lot of people probably do things without thinking," Ellie said. "I just didn't think about it, maybe because if I had thought about it I wouldn't have done it, and I'm glad I did it."

The roommate gave Ellie a sharp look. "I didn't think you were that interested in politics."

"I'm not. I guess I did it because I wanted to do something. Now I've done something."

"Well, you didn't do much. They won't even put you on pro. Just give you a warning. You didn't do much."

"Maybe I should do something else, then," Ellie said, as someone entered the room to tell her she had a phone call. The caller was Shapiro, to ask if she had gotten one of the letters. It was he who told her that only five had received them and that she was, or soon would be, part of a university-wide *cause célèbre*. Would she meet with the other four "to plan what to do"?

"There isn't anything we can do, is there? I mean, what could we do?"

That, Shapiro told her, was what the meeting was for. Would she come? Yes, she would, Ellie replied, not thinking again. Shapiro was political and she was not political. There would be an awful lot of talk, and a lot of it would probably be from Roger Elias, so it would be loud and with lots of dirty words. There was nothing wrong with dirty words, but she wasn't used to them and they made her uncomfortable. Her parents said a well-educated person could express himself without them. And she would probably be the only girl, and they were radicals—wasn't SDS radical? Which would mean there would be no end to it. It was even possible there could be expulsions, but maybe getting expelled would be better than staying here and getting graduated.

Ellie had never known anyone who'd gotten expelled. She'd known kids who'd dropped out or transferred, and girls who'd taken a semester off to have a baby. She'd known a boy who'd broken a leg in a skiing accident, and she'd had a girl friend who'd been killed in a traffic accident. There were two black boys at school who said they'd been to jail for robbery before they were rescued by the war on poverty. You couldn't tell whether to believe them or not, but she didn't really know them, so basically she was the first person she'd ever met who was in trouble.

Ellie gave her hair four hundred brush strokes, poured oil in her bath before soaking herself in it, got out, rubbed skin balm over her body, rolled on her deodorant, powdered herself, slipped on silk and lace, sat down in front of a mirror and gave twenty minutes to making up her eyes and face, put on a mostly expensive outfit, and went to the meeting. The other four were there, as were some other students, a lawyer, and Sil, who was looking longer and hairier and dirtier than usual. Ellie decided he was more offensive than Roger, who acted as she thought he would. She said nothing but agreed to everything they decided after hours of arguing, namely that none of the Norman Thomas Five would act independently, that they would insist on one joint interview with Associate Dean McTavish instead of the five separate ones the letters called for, that they would insist on having the lawyer with them, and that before the interview there should be a rally outside Rennecker Hall, where the Dean's office was located, and that all of this should be given to the *Daily Review* to publicize the next confrontation.

They asked Ellie if she'd mimeograph a stencil, so they'd have something to pass out on campus telling people what was going on. She said she would, and Ellie, who always made good on her commitments, did. It was while she was passing out the broadsides that she had her second conversation with Yaldell. She hadn't meant to offer him one— that might have been rude—but she was passing out so many, she'd stopped looking at the faces of the people coming in and out of the Union. Yaldell offered to buy her a cup of coffee in the Owl Cove, and she accepted in a pleasant, pretty way.

"Ellie," he said, "don't you think you're making a bit much of this? Dean McTavish only wants to have a talk with you."

"Roger Elias says that he has no right to question people about their political activities."

"What do you say?"

"Mr. Yaldell, I've gone this far, so I might as well keep going."

"But why, Ellie? I don't think you're very political, are you?"

"That's what my roommate said. I guess not. I did go on the Spring Peace March to the Amphitheater."

"Well, so did I. I wouldn't be surprised if a quarter of the University marched, but this is different."

"I know, but they should've been allowed to have their meeting."

"Well, Ellie, I don't think they'll be disciplined if they go in and talk, but I don't understand you. You're not involved in politics. You seem so calm about the whole thing. You don't appear to have any ideas of your own. You tell me what Roger Elias thinks, not what you think. Look, Ellie, you admit you're not political. Did it ever occur to you that you could be used by people who are?"

"Does it matter, Mr. Yaldell?" Ellie asked back at him, and the pleasant smile on her face gave way to a serious expression.

"I think it matters a great deal. Ellie, I know you know these aren't normal times. People are pretty excited by the war and a lot of other things. A well-meaning gesture could possibly contribute to—well, I don't know, but things happen, incidents. I think it's important to know if you're being used or not."

Ellie may have faintly shaken her head. She made some motion with it and replied in a voice that had a foreign tone in it, one of despair or sadness. "You can't be used if you're doing what you think you should do. It doesn't matter what other people make of it. It doesn't matter if it happens to agree with what Roger Elias might want, or, well, if it's something you might not like, as long as it's what I think I should do, and, I don't know, but, well, now that it's done or I did it, well, I can see I couldn't go on as I was."

Yaldell had a puzzled expression on his face. "You couldn't go on as you were?"

"I mean going to class, writing papers. I mean living here just going on and the school just going on and on. Mr. Yaldell, I have to go now."

She left him with his coffee, repeating to himself, ". . . 'and the school just going on and on.' What the hell does that mean?"

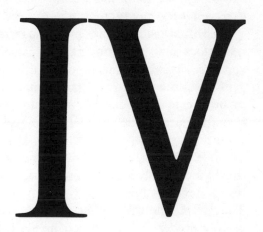

IV

WHILE ELLIE RECTOR was straining to get through inarticulate layers of politeness, routine, and her sense of obligation to the people and practices of a growing up she'd begun to mistrust, a collateral event was developing on campus and in Washington, D.C. In the Verbal History Project transcripts there are only occasional allusions to it. Evidently, it was thought of as an adult affair, with no particular connection to the crisis, a mess which hardly did credit to the University, one peripheral to the institution which didn't concern most of its students.

If the students made it a concern, that fact isn't known. As the crisis worsened there were a number of surveys of student-faculty opinion. But none inquired if the Sparkle toothpaste business contributed to the developing sense of disrespect and demoralization that stripped the place of its awe, of the institutional majesty that the cut-stone pilasters and elaborate iron fences and fixtures were meant to impart. There must have been some impact, even if it was unmeasured, because for the two or three days during which Sparkle toothpaste was a page-one item, the students and faculty had a unique, extended opportunity to study Martin Hungerford.

Television made a culprit of Hungerford. He came on the six-o'clock news looking nothing like the gowned figure in velvet cowl and mortarboard treading behind marshals, regents, trustees, provosts, chancellors, doctors, and docents to preside at convocations, there to bestow degrees, adulthood, a place in the world from a high chair resembling a throne.

On television he was in a business suit, a fuzzy, oldish man, drawn indistinctly by electronic lines. After a day or so even his friends were bothered by the impression he was making. They were astonished that words which sounded so judiciously prudent when uttered in his office were evasive on TV, that he came across as inept—hypocritical, but worst of all, inept.

He was disadvantaged by the scene, a single man at a table looking upward at six semi-circular senatorial faces. It was a television tableau a generation could recognize. They had placed him where the investigated, the exposed, the denounced, the reprobated have sat explaining, sulking, embarrassed, indignant, taking the Fifth, whispering to their lawyers, pleading to be put in their own context, gangsters, Klansmen, communists, sinking politicians, unlucky lobbyists, Minutemen, cornered monopolists, spies, swindlers, connivers, influence men.

Now Dr. Martin Hungerford. But he had not been brought to the bar straining and pulling to escape. He hadn't been subpoenaed but had come voluntarily, having written the committee asking to appear to testify in favor of the new patent law. He had no hint that one of the Senators was delighted and waiting for him. The others didn't care at all, too indifferent to defend him or to ask more than an idle question. They came and went during the hearings, slipping off to other marble and wainscotted places, coming back to read their mail while one Senator harried Hungerford.

Hungerford had come to Washington to tell the Senators he was in favor of a bill that would indefinitely extend the patent and ownership rights on a wide variety of inventions and discoveries. His statement was routine, a dull thing prepared by the representative of a trade association, put into the stately language of public service and broadly pompous policy that university presidents are thought to speak in. Then the Senator had at him, as the transcript shows.

THE SENATOR: Dr. Hungerford, does your institution have a direct interest in this legislation?

HUNGERFORD: Scientists working in the laboratories of many universities make discoveries, which are subsequently patented by the school in question and then licensed. At some institutions it's a valuable source of income, Senator.

THE SENATOR: I was asking if your institution would profit from this law? Does your university benefit from such patents?

HUNGERFORD: Not directly.

THE SENATOR: You're being ingenuous, Dr. Hungerford. I think you know that I'm asking about a substance with the trade name of Corex-B, exclusively licensed for use in Sparkle toothpaste, manufactured by Willard Brothers, International. As I understand it, Doctor, your university makes a certain amount of money from every tube of Sparkle sold. Now, what I'd like to know is how much money do you make? How did it come about that the University is participating in this arrangement and what is your relationship to Willard Brothers, International?

HUNGERFORD: I thought the nature of the University's participation in Corex-B royalties was very well known. The inventor of Corex-B, Dr. Hamilcar Mosconi, has given the University forty per cent—I believe it is—of the royalties. Since Dr. Mosconi is not a graduate of our University, nor a member of the faculty, I think this generous endowment is particularly laudable, Senator.

THE SENATOR: I don't. I think it's a patent medicine swindle, Dr. Hungerford, and that you and your University have lent your names to something you shouldn't have, because you wanted the money. I don't mean you personally profited, Dr. Hungerford, just that you, shall I say, exercised the powers of your office without due care.

On TV sets with good reception and especially fine picture resolution it was possible to see the old man's eyelids go up and down. He was silent, looking at the Senator, several of whose colleagues thought this might be interesting enough to warrant stopping their whispering and paper shuffling. Hungerford continued to say nothing, although several times he swelled up as though he might, but then he deflated himself and maintained his silence.

THE SENATOR: Those aren't nice things to say. I suppose that's what you're thinking, Dr. Hungerford. I agree, but they're true and I'm going to prove them.

HUNGERFORD: What's true? And what are you going to prove, Senator? The arrangement between Dr. Mosconi, the University, and Willard Brothers, International, is quite common in higher education. There's nothing singular about it, quite ordinary, quite.

THE SENATOR: Let's go through this thing point by point, Dr. Hungerford. Dr. Mosconi's doctorate is self-awarded, as far as I've been able to determine. Three years prior to his arrangement with you, he was doing business under the name of Hamilton Mosconi. Then this same gentleman marketed Corex-A as a cough syrup, which was impounded and destroyed by the Food and Drug Administration as a dangerous substance, one particularly harmful to people suffering from a wide range of disorders, including certain kinds of heart disease, hepatitis, and mononucleosis.

HUNGERFORD: Naturally, I haven't brought my records with me. I'd have to consult them before I could comment, Senator.

THE SENATOR: Would your records contain this information?

HUNGERFORD: Well, I can't say. They might, no, I suppose they wouldn't.

THE SENATOR: Would you bring them back for the committee tomorrow, Doctor?

The six-o'clock news cut to other subjects here. Not many people on campus saw the show, but the word got around and by the eleven-o'clock repeat the audience was significantly larger. Myron Mirsky recalls that it was after watching the show that he coined the expression, "the daily atrocity." Whether it was original with him or not, it soon came into vogue as a stock response to every move the Administration made.

Another person who watched the eleven-o'clock repeat was Martin Hungerford. He did it in his Washington hotel room. This fact, his reactions, and most everything else that took place is well, if not reliably, known, because shortly after the old man left the Senate he called the University and asked a brilliant, blabby, young law school professor to take the first plane and join him. The professor told his wife what happened. She gave everybody an inaccurate account, so he had to straighten all their friends out and give them the facts —"which were crazy enough without embroidery," he would add, rebuking his wife and heightening his listeners' desire to hear at the same time.

"Naturally, if Hungerford were a client, I couldn't reveal any of this. You have to understand that. I wasn't retained by him as a lawyer but asked to come to Washington and give my advice as a faculty member," he said every time he told the story. It was the kind of ethical definition certain academic types like to make.

"It would have been funny if it hadn't been sad in a way. I knocked on the hotel room door, there's Hungerford in slippers, telling me to be quiet, that he's on TV. So he sits there watching himself get slit up the tummy and, my God, when it's over, he says, 'I've put on a little weight. You can see it around the jowls, but anyway, I think I made that member of the United States Senate veer off a little, eh? The man wants to be another Estes Kefauver, but of course he doesn't have the stuff for it, going around pouncing on people at random. I think I handled him correctly, treated him with the respect due his office, but coldly, with dignity.'

"If I hadn't known for a fact that Martin Hungerford has no sense of humor whatsoever, I would have said he had to be joking. It took me a while to figure what was with him, but he made sense. The self-deception of the innocent: he owns no stock in Willard Brothers, International.

"I gave him a curbstone legal opinion that neither he nor the University was liable for whatever kind of poison might be in Corex-B. He got a little stuffy about that and absolutely began to pout when I said what he needed was a good public relations man, or a fixer to get the Senator to forget about the whole business. What I was worried about was how it would look on TV when it came out he's a member of Willard's board and that Maxwell Iverson, the president of Willard, mind you, is on the University's board of trustees. You know how he is. You can't come out and tell him he's going to look like he was played for a sucker and maneuvered into huckstering for a toothpaste. Say that and he'd either pout, shut up entirely, or say something idiotic, like, 'We're all gentlemen here.' Nothing quite that asinine, but you can't get through to him. I can't even understand how that brain works. I look at him and I see a nice, old, stuffy guy, who should be on a lawn with an English sheepdog watching his grandchildren play hide-and-go-seek.

"That night he didn't know what they were going to pull on him the next day, or I'm sure he wouldn't have been so bland, sitting there congratulating himself, worrying about his weight problem, and telling me what he told the Senator. He must have said it half a dozen times. 'University presidents sit on boards of directors of many major corporations. Quite unexceptional, positively.' Then he'd puff, look impressive, let the air out of himself, and turn into a confused-looking old man, and then he'd go at it again. 'Heyns of Berkeley is on the board of Hunt Foods; Killian of MIT is on General Motors; Kirk of Columbia is on IBM, and Miller at Northwestern is on Sears, Roebuck. Happens all the time, all the time.' You know how he talks, everything ad hominem, little bursts of ooze that can't be questioned.

"I almost said to him, when he gave me that business, 'But you don't see Killian on the boob tube offering no money down and slashing prices on Chevrolets.' You can't say that to him. You'd just hurt his feelings. I wanted to, though, and maybe I should have. While he was talking I remembered that unbelievable scene in his office when they announced the Corex-B deal. Him and that phony, Hamilcar Mosconi— God, what a con man he's turned out to be—and Iverson and those whores from Flexner Research Hospital, all being introduced to the camera, and the crap he was handing out! He was really puffed up that day, but can you imagine the president of one of America's most important universities saying that junk will cut cavities by ninety percent, and what a boon to mankind? Now it turns out it saves your teeth but ruins your heart. There must be another way to get money for a school without doing this. That's why you have to feel sorry for him. He sells toothpaste so we can teach.

"Did you know this university maintains a full-time agent in Washington? He arrived about midnight—just as I thought

I'd convinced Hungerford that he should disown Hamilcar—to say that wouldn't be necessary because he'd gotten two Senators who were going to attack *the* Senator tomorrow. I told him he was crazy. He didn't even bother to answer me. He was too preoccupied, strutting around Hungerford's hotel room lecturing to him. 'Remember, Dr. Hungerford,' he said —and I'll never forget it because he had one finger up in the air like he'd just split the atom—'Remember, you are a university—science, learning, scholarship, commitment! These people are politicians. Stand on what you are and remember they don't dare give you a hard time or America isn't going to get to the moon.' Hungerford blew himself up again, nodded, and emitted some lofty, self-deprecating unction about how 'I wouldn't go quite so far, but it's certainly true the modern university has a particularly important and multifaceted role to play in our society.' "

Despite the Washington agent, the six-o'clock news was a catastrophe for Hungerford. The agent's two Senators had appeared to support the University, but that footage didn't make the air. What did was the Senator telling Hungerford that the pharmacologist who'd tested and certified Corex-B was a staff member at Flexner Research Hospital and also was paid a considerable sum every year as a consultant to Willard Brothers, International. Testimony by two men from the Food and Drug Administration to the effect that the Corex-B tests run at Flexner Research Hospital were worthless didn't get on the air, but was printed in the papers the next day. Nearly two minutes of the final exchange between the Senator and Hungerford were shown, however, and greedily watched by students and faculty.

HUNGERFORD: Senator, ours is one of the most distinguished scientific faculties in the world. Not only does it boast seven Nobel laureates, but—

THE SENATOR: Dr. Hungerford, excuse me for interrupting,

but I'm not questioning the ability of your faculty, only the role your school played in purveying to the public a dangerous substance for general consumption. I am questioning the role of one of your faculty members and a member of your board of trustees, both of whom had an obvious conflict of interest.

HUNGERFORD: The fact that one of our faculty members was retained by Willard is quite ordinary, quite. Nothing unusual in it. A large number of our faculty consult with many companies, and, I might add, Senator, with the United States government. The fact that they do, that they are sought after, is evidence of their distinction and competence. As for the role Mr. Iverson played, I can assure you there was no conflict of interest whatsoever. When the question of accepting the Sparkle toothpaste royalties came before the University's Board of Trustees, Mr. Iverson abstained both from voting or taking part in the discussion, as the minutes of the meeting indicate.

THE SENATOR: You don't think Mr. Iverson exploited his position on the board to come up with a magnificent advertising gimmick, a toothpaste certified as something just short of miraculous by one of this country's most renowned institutions of higher learning? You don't think that?

HUNGERFORD: I think it is possible to put a dishonorable construction on any human act.

THE SENATOR: And you're suggesting that's what I did? Put a dishonorable construction on a simple, philanthropic endeavor? And you're not going to do anything about Corex-B? You're going to have your people come down here and lobby to have it put back on the market?

HUNGERFORD: We certainly shall look into the matter. It's possible our tests of Corex-B failed to pick up, ah, drawbacks to its use, that other tests may have. That's science, Senator, testing and correction. Checking and forming new hypotheses.

THE SENATOR: You're going back and you're going to study it, is that it, Doctor?

HUNGERFORD: Yes, Senator, that's what we do at a University. We study things.

The blabby law professor reported that Hungerford watched both the six- and the eleven-o'clock news, completely satisfied about everything to do with his appearance but the fat on his jowls. The pharmacologist from Flexner had arrived and repetitiously explained that the Senator didn't know what he was talking about. "Certainly not, certainly not. Quite outside his field of competence. Doesn't know anything about it," Hungerford agreed. The University's Washington agent said he had information that another toothpaste company had fed the Senator the material on Corex-B and Hamilcar Mosconi. The professor caught a late plane back home, so there is no more gossip about Hungerford's reaction to the third day of television exposure.

The University did put out a press release under Hungerford's name, which was printed in the *Daily Review* and the metropolitan newspapers, saying that "the public should understand that the government has not ordered Sparkle toothpaste or Corex-B withdrawn from sale and that as far as is known, the claims made for this remarkable agent of preventive dentistry are correct. However, because of any possible confusion in the public's mind and to make certain there have been no errors, the University will shortly undertake a new set of tests." Willard Brothers, International, stock dropped a couple of points, and the talk around town had it that the company's advertising agency was saying the advantages of the University's connection had been impaired. It was rumored the agency was suggesting that Sparkle's name be changed to Bright White.

On the campus there were no definite reactions to the Washington revelations. Some talk about it at the Faculty Club, but little you could put your finger on. A few men wondered if the deans and department chairmen were keeping close enough tabs on outside consultancies. There was a regulation or statute or some kind of rule in the compendious University codes stating that all outside work of a professional nature was to be approved by the department chairman and the appropriate set of deans. It had sometimes been a practice to evade giving raises by suggesting that people moonlight—"Of course, George, the committee thinks you're entitled to a raise, but I don't think the department's going to get its budget increase this year. Take a dry promotion. A full associateship—I think I can get that through, that'll help you. A man from an institution like this gets a lot of offers."

Sil was the only person who was moved to do anything. He clomped up to Monique's, followed by the Fuckheads, "who are spiritual bikeriders and social acrobats, theatrical types." The Fuckheads said they possessed a rudimentary form of organization and claimed several leaders based in another part of the city. When around the University they followed Sil, fetching for him and playing parts in his charades.

"Slob Child, you are a slut," Sil shouted at Monique. "Get outta my way."

"Don't hurt my pussies," the girl said, scampering around, pulling her sleeping bag out of the way and picking up the cats' food dishes. She looked like a witch. She wore a long skirt down to her ankles, and sometimes she'd hunch up when she was moving around her apartment talking to herself.

"I'm going to coopt cooptation. Going to merchandise and package the product," Sil said, while the other young men made trips downstairs to bring up tools and materials. "Roll some joints for us, Slob Child, and don't feed any grass to your cats," Sil ordered her. Shapiro had tried to break Sil of marijuana smoking but couldn't. He disapproved of the stuff on principle and was always worried about the police planting it on him and arresting him for possession. Out of deference, Sil usually didn't smoke it around Shapiro, but he often did while he worked. He said as long as he was high he never had to sleep, and that it improved his concentration. It had the opposite effect on Slob Child and Sil's assistants, but Sil labored on, muttering about "coopting cooptation" and making a "consumers' Mardi Gras." When he was finished, he had constructed a set of very large objects designed to be worn by the Fuckheads. The first was an eight-foot-high Sparkle toothpaste tube; then there was an enormous, smiling set of teeth; a giant pack of cigarettes with a label identifying them as Columbia Cancer-Proof Filter Tips; a horrible bacillus to which was attached a sign announcing it had been invented for biological warfare at the University of Pennsylvania; an unpleasant thing that appeared to be illuminated from somewhere within itself—its sign said it was a cancer-of-the-ass cell; lastly was a tear almost as large as the toothpaste tube. It was constructed so that as you saw it from various angles, tortured, screaming faces appeared, straining to break out of the plastic.

The whole walking exhibit, which Sil called "The Supermarket Is a Boon to Mankind," was ready on the morning of the day of the rally for the Norman Thomas Five. It appeared on campus in the early afternoon, led by Sil, who was wearing a mask of a grotesque Martin Hungerford. He had his motion picture camera and the Supermarket had leaflets urging people to come to the rally in front of Rennecker Hall, where many of the deans and the student social services were located.

Yaldell didn't see the Supermarket, but even without it there had been signs. The president of the Conservative Alliance had told him his group had voted to attend the rally and support the protest "as long as it's lawful and orderly, of course." Several members of the student government had said much the same thing, with one boy remarking, "I guess that's what the University gets for never having taken us seriously." All this intelligence was passed along on the phone to Blackie McTavish, with the remark that something was afoot.

"Well, what?" Blackie wanted to know.

"I can't say exactly," Yaldell answered, trying to put his impressions into communicable form.

"Think they're up to something and not telling you? That it? A secret tactic?" Blackie was pressing for something specific to use before talking to Dean Pomfret, a job that won him Yaldell's sympathy. "I know college boys," Pomfret loved to say. College girls were excluded, perhaps because in the Dean's experience—he was two years from retirement —college girls almost never got into trouble. "Oh, you talk about riots and such. I have to chuckle. My Lord, I can recall some unbelievable episodes here, right in the Square. You'd have thought they were going to burn down the college. At the risk of sounding like an old, old man—and I know that's a sin now, to be nearer the grave than the next fellow—I sometimes think the only useful thing I've learned—I'm talking about personal facts—is that the world didn't start with me. It's an exasperating thing to tell the young, that there isn't too much new under the sun, the atomic theory being as old as Democritus, that entire lecture, oft repeated, it's exasperating, but it's not given by us old men just to make the young feel small and inconsequential. If you remember it, you remember to suspend judgment, keep your balance, and let things work themselves out naturally, as they often do. Take that from an old man, if not as something proved, take it on faith."

This lecture enraged Blackie McTavish more than it enraged the undergraduates. "Things don't always work themselves out for the best," Blackie would say, while the men students would remark of Pomfret, "He's a nice old guy," and the coeds declare, "He's cute." Pomfret also had the reputation of being an easy, forgiving disciplinarian who'd talk your ear off, reminiscing about the University—he'd been there more than forty years—and then conclude by saying, "You won't let it happen again, I'm sure, so let's pretend it didn't happen, all right?"

It was said that short of murder, Dean Pomfret wouldn't throw anybody out of school. He was unperturbable. Bad marks ("Good grades and scholarship have an accidental connection to my way of thinking"), drinking bouts, marijuana ("I'm sure the college boy of the past would have experimented with it, if only he'd known about it"), sex ("Nothing you can do about that except keep it as much out of sight as possible. That's why I always tell these unfortunate girls who've gone too far they should drop out for a semester and have their babies"), radical politics ("We've had that before"). The trick was to get in to see Pomfret to be forgiven by him, but it wasn't easy. There was Blackie McTavish, the Dean of Men, the Dean of Women, and an entire corps of sub-deans to skirt first.

Blackie McTavish, who had hopes of succeeding Pomfret, didn't look on him as a benign noodlehead to be led and manipulated in the last months before his retirement. The Verbal History Project brings this out with considerable clarity. McTavish was very frank in portions of his interview, possibly because he wanted to cut clear of the disaster and save his own career. But the transcript shows serious disagreements with Pomfret that must have long antedated the campus upheaval. Some of the tension between the two men was generational. McTavish, twenty years younger, shows himself as a hard-line rationalist who is skeptical that things work out. In his opinion, you have to arrange to work things out, and that requires effort, planning, sacrifice, and self-discipline, a point of view you might expect from a man who was a line infantry officer in World War II, came home to do his graduate work, and went off again to see combat in Korea. Pomfret had been too young or too old for the great international massacres of the twentieth century. But most of this comes through in the McTavish transcript:

MC TAVISH: First, I want to say that I admire Dean Pomfret. I have great respect for him, and until relatively recently the system that he built for handling student affairs worked very well. It has been criticized as manipulative and patronizing, without any procedure in the quasi-legal sense of that term. I agree, but there's an important qualification. It was a system that fit well with the student body we had here until the end of the Second World War, and I think it was at least adequate until four or five years ago.

Until the early or middle fifties, this campus was dominated by the undergraduate college, whose students were mostly from comfortable or upper-class families. For them Dean Pomfret's system worked well. We had *in loco parentis*, we had lots of rules, we had subordinates do the dirty work. They made the punishments and he mitigated them. A lot of people think of Dean Pomfret as a fuzzy, sweet gentleman who doesn't have the heart to expel a student. That's not true. Dean Pomfret is foxy—he built that image of himself, because it worked well with the student body we had here. They didn't consider themselves adults. They expected to be treated in that sort of paternal way, and I think it was the right way to treat naughty fraternity boys who went on panty raids and cheated in their French finals. In those days we were a finishing school for the upper classes—not exclusively, but that was a major part of our work. Read the college catalogue of thirty years ago; it talks about the University as a "character-building" institution, inculcating good morals.

That's all dead and gone. We're a "meritocracy" now. That's what Joseph Gusfield, the sociologist, calls the modern university. Very few boys can buy their way into this place today, and none of them can stay in on money or social position. Academic merit is the key factor. To my mind, that means an adjustment in the Dean of Students' office. It means fewer rules, but those carefully written and enforced by equitable procedures. Due process, in other words. It means introducing the same kind of rationality here in Rennecker Hall that you'll find in most of the rest of this school.

In my opinion Dean Pomfret never recognized the changes that had taken place here. He was still operating on the paternal model of a gentlemen's academy. Oh, we use computers in this office, but our underlying organization and approach was that of the thirties and forties. For example, although I urged Dean Pomfret to have regular meetings of the deans' staffs, he preferred to deal with people on a one-to-one basis, inviting them to his club or home to dinner. That was fine when there were only a handful of people here, but we occupy a whole building! A whole building! And under his system internal communications, coherent policy development have broken down.

What I'm trying to say is that even before we had this crisis I believe we were doing a sub-par job. When the crisis hit, we couldn't handle it. As the trouble on the campus got worse, Rennecker Hall fell into paralyzed, contradictory anarchy. At least that's my opinion.

INTERVIEWER: Do you think, say, if you'd been able to carry out your organizational ideas you could have averted the crisis?

MC TAVISH: That's a large order. My answer would have to be that we couldn't have held it off entirely, but I think its proportions, I mean the hugeness of the thing, would have been cut down. You see, our errors, not only during the crisis but before, put fuel on the fire. These kids were running around screaming that the place was run like

Kafka's castle. One of the most used words about the University was "Kafkaesque." They had a point, and it's what can be expected when you have irrational men running an institution of this size with computers. I mean, if you're a crooked, illogical thinker, the computer you're running isn't going to cover up for you. No, what it's going to do is magnify your irrationality. We'd programmed our computer to print out the craziest, most arbitrary things, which enraged many students who ordinarily wouldn't touch an organization like SDS. I'm talking about the majority of students who believe in the meritocracy. They could see that we weren't following the meritocratic administrative principles. Eccentricity was practiced in major areas like raising student fees and then forgiving payments on a helter-skelter basis so that two students with nearly the same grades and financial situation would be paying different amounts. Paternalism.

INTERVIEWER: Did that happen often?

MC TAVISH: To be honest, no. Financial aid had been evenly distributed except for cases that went personally over Dean Pomfret's desk, but my point is you don't need many cases to cause trouble. And what were we supposed to say about these inequalities? That it was an exception because the boy managed to get in to see the Dean of Students, who took a liking to him and waived the fees?

INTERVIEWER: People on campus say that Dean Pomfret's exceptions were mostly black students. It that so?

MC TAVISH: I think so. He was always forward looking in this area. He extended himself personally . . . surprising in a man his age. He went recruiting for students into ghetto high schools. Black students could always get in to see him immediately, but even there we had no overall program, a higgledy-piggledy of overlapping, ad hoc expedients. I don't want to detract from Dean Pomfret's leadership in this area. He was a prime mover, even when there was no interest, back in the time when the University—well, all schools—failed to live up to their responsibilities.

INTERVIEWER: Then in some ways Dean Pomfret was progressive?

MC TAVISH: Certainly, in many ways. He pioneered setting up student psychiatric services. He did many things, made many important contributions to this school and to university administration in general. My criticism is that his style remained, well, I said "paternal"—I believe that's the word I used. And I think he underestimated the force of student radicalism. Equated it to panty raids and the fraternity hazing of his own youth. He belittled it as a national and international movement. Nathan Glazer out at Berkeley calls it a new Luddite movement, the modern equivalent of the displaced handicraft workers who smashed the machines in the first factories. That doesn't make them less dangerous. Glazer was one of the first to suggest, after Berkeley, that the student radicals might decide on a scorched-earth policy before they withdrew. That's why I was what you might call a hard-liner on this thing, before, during, and afterward. I still am. That's why I disagreed with Dean Pomfret. I believed we should have had a well worked-out policy, a contingency sort of thing, ready to be put into effect fast. He didn't, so we didn't. Our hour came, we went down as they did at Berkeley and Columbia.

At four o'clock there were a thousand students in front of Rennecker Hall with the Norman Thomas Five, the heads of a number of student organizations, including the president of the Conservative Alliance, and sympathetic faculty members. The speeches had begun at 3:30 and were continuing. The audience, standing, seemed prepared to listen indefinitely while the leaders speechified and argued among themselves. Roger and Shapiro were arguing about what to do while people from less radical groups denounced the Administration.

"You make radicals by committing radical acts. You're not going to keep these people by doing nothing. Give 'em a few speeches so they get their rocks off an' go home? What happens then? What's next? Nothing. Stop scratching your damn hair, Shapiro," Roger said in a voice that was both a yell and a whisper.

"So what do you propose," Shapiro said back at him, and then was shocked that he didn't hear Roger's answer. He saw his mouth moving, felt the shower of energy out of Roger that dropped and sprinkled all over him, but he was so overcome by the force of the speech he blanked on its content. A fast sequence of recurring Roger-thoughts detonated in his brain: animal / but not political animal / animal-animal / mathematical animal / burn-out while they're young animal / leaping animal has no tail / has to leap animal / his mass derives through his energy / hate animals.

Roger left him to take over the speaking—splendid, charismatic bullshit, the student as nigger again, the nigger as nigger, the soldier as nigger, Uncle Hungerford, "in the words of Mario Savio, we'll bring this university to a grinding halt," the war and the computer, the diddly and the daddly of living every day in the smog we breathe, the cancer we smoke, swimming in our polluted rivers, picnicking on our deforested hills, is this all, is this all for children whose treasure on earth is already stored up for them and who do no banking with an anthropomorphic, ethnocentric God?

Most of the windows of Rennecker Hall had faces in them, looking down and listening. Secretaries, minor functionaries atingle with bracing indignation as the words splashed on them; McTavish finding confirmation of what he thought; Pomfret feeling both disapproval and sympathy but staying behind a curtain so he couldn't be seen; and the lesser deans and third-echelon fellows from the bursar's office, chattering, "So there's our Mark Rudd. Savio had more class—and he didn't talk dirty. Can you believe what he's saying? I can't believe he's saying it." Shapiro fretted and looked for signs of the audience turning against Roger.

"He's crazy, doesn't know where to begin or when to stop," he said to Sil, who'd come up to Shapiro twisting his wrists in opposite directions as he wound his movie camera.

"Man, Roger's crazy. See, that's what gives him that sense, like in those Mongolian tribes, or wherever they have it, ya know, it's the crazy one who has contact with the spirits, that's the one who knows when's the time to plant the corn or hunt the buffalo or walrus, man, or the wild yak, whatever they do. It's the crazy one who's got the contact, see, like Roger, doesn't know when to begin, just feels it and then he does it. He sleeps a lot, I'll bet. They do. He'll sleep tonight, drop on his bed, sleep fifteen hours. The Slob Child, she gets contacts sometimes in a situation and when it's over, she sleeps hours, fifteen hours, twenty-four, a whole day. I don't trust crazy people, though. I'm with you," Sil said, and slipped off.

Shapiro dawdled in his head. He knew he couldn't match Roger at his energy peaks, but they didn't sustain themselves. Then he would get up and say, "Thank you, Brother Elias," and give them a sensible radical critique, a clear statement, reasoned and proportionate, entitled, "Where We Are Now," by Ray Shapiro, twenty cents, Freedom Publications, a compelling analysis of university complicity with warfare imperialism, showing the systemic origins of racism and the crying need to do something before we choke on ourselves, or it might be "Art Mind / Political Fact: The Radical Aesthetic of Sil," by Ray Shapiro, one dollar with color plates of the E. J. Cornford Contraption and The Supermarket Is a Boon to Mankind, demolishes once and for all the value-free attack on the New Left as passion without program. Shapiro is a social thinker who dares to dream of what he calls the "self-realizing society."

Cheering and much applause. Roger was calling out and the amplified echoes were feeding back to him, "Put your body where your mouth is, mouth is, is," and Ellie Rector had taken the microphone and was shouting, "No More! Let's not have it any more." The crowd began the chant, "No More, No More," which the people in the windows fumbled with. "No More? What's that mean?" "No, they're saying no war, that's what they're chanting." About seventy-five people were following Roger into the building for the sit-in. Sil was already up on a ledge taking pictures of the breach across the threshold as Shapiro forced his way to Roger's side.

"Roger, what are you doing, what are you doing?"

"I'm doing. That's enough."

"It isn't enough, damn it. You've left the army outside. They're not following you. We never discussed this," Shapiro said, but Roger had turned away from him to tell his followers to wait there while he went upstairs to demand Pomfret come out and talk in full public hearing. Around Shapiro students were slipping their backs down the walls until they came to sitting positions on the floor, where they talked quietly or read books. One foursome began a bridge game. Shapiro stayed on his feet, talking to some of the other radical youths who were also complaining. "This is ridiculous. We don't know why we're here. Let's get a discussion going. This has no connection with the war or racism or anything. What the hell do we want to have a confrontation with Dean Pomfret for? Shapiro, Roger's gotta be controlled. He's acting like Moses."

"Moses had a map and marching order," Shapiro replied, looking for Ellie, who was outside the building with another girl, peeking in.

For an hour everything wallowed inconclusively. The crowd outside began to thin, but the majority hung around, talking to each other more than they were listening to the speakers. It would quiet down from time to time as Roger would come out or appear in a second-story window to say, "Pomfret must face the people." While this was happening, "the daily atrocity" was preparing itself.

Pomfret had left the building having, according to everybody's account in the Verbal History Project, said to leave the demonstration alone and do nothing except make sure the office doors were locked and that there was no vandalism. These instructions resulted in a call to campus security, which sent over two men in a university police car. Out of pure laziness, the men parked the car by the side of the front entrance to Rennecker Hall, somewhat in between the crowd, now down to half its original size, and the building. There was a little catcalling when the officers appeared, but after it became apparent no other police were going to be called, people forgot about them. The guards went inside and stood around, listening to the students debate what they were going to do.

Roger had lost most of his support. People were listening to Shapiro and running to the crowd outside carrying the message, "They're coming. They'll be out in a few minutes."

As he got the worst of it, Roger began losing interest. He stood against a wall, his head tilting back, looking at the ceiling and letting his friends argue that they should stay there until Pomfret came back. "Vote! Vote!" people replied, hungry and impatient at the repetition. They did, and the sit-in was over. Whereupon the daily atrocity happened. People were moving out the doors and the two guards were encouraging them, saying, "Okay, it's all over. Let's all go eat supper," when someone objected to their tone. A movement to turn back into the building, a shout, another shout, a door being pushed open and closed, then the two guards, a hand on each arm, were taking Shapiro to the car.

"Look, I didn't say anything to you guys. Why are you busting me?" Shapiro said, but they made no answer. "Oh, hell, okay, so arrest me," he said, "a perfect end to a delightfully crummy day."

Some of the sit-inners reversed themselves and went back in. The people in front of the crowd made a lowing, negative noise, while those in the rear strained on tiptoes or asked each other what was going on. The police put Shapiro inside the car, where he threw his arms out and his head back in disgusted fatigue. It came in on him just then that he was not a revolutionary but a liberal reformer, maybe a little more to the left than his dad, but still not so much. This thought came to him as a relief, but at that second the revolution, rebellion, uprising was coming into being. Outside, The Supermarket Is a Boon to Mankind had surrounded the police car. The Sparkle toothpaste tube was dancing on the roof—Shapiro could hear it—the package of Columbia Cancer Proof Filter Tips was revolving around on the hood—Shapiro could see it—the war germ was rocking the rear bumper—Shapiro could feel it, and the tear from the eye of screaming humanity, Shapiro wondered where the tear might be.

The crowd saw and moved, coming around the car, sitting down and encircling it. For the next twenty-three hours, Shapiro was the man in the car.

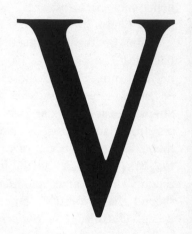

THE SUPREME CREAM—Sil had tagged the beautiful young man with the name—was at the edge of the crowd when he figured out what had happened and where Shapiro was. He turned, a book satchel over one shoulder, the other arm straight out as a stabilizer, and did *grande jetés* across the sitting protestors. In the car window the Supreme Cream's head went looking for Shapiro.

"All right?" he asked. Shapiro nodded yes. "Climb out this side and you can get away," the Supreme Cream suggested, making a quick little gesture toward what was happening on the side of the car.

The two police were being quietly pushed and baited by four or five male students who were out of phase with the crowd, which was quiet and watching The Supermarket Is a Boon to Mankind do an impromptu mime. The boys were pushing up against the campus policemen with swelled out chests. The two older men were forced to lean back so far their pulled-in jaws made double chins. "Pig," the boys said in a mumbled whisper. "Your wife sucks. His mother sucks, too."

"Come on," the Supreme Cream urged, "they can't stop you, Ray. You can get clean away."

"No."

"Why not? You can't stay there."

"I didn't do anything. They're busting me for nothing. If I run they can bust me later for resisting arrest or running away . . . besides, I'm here. Let's see if we can't get something out of it."

"Huh?" The Supreme Cream's handsome face registered lack of understanding. It was Sil who once said of him, "Man, don't ever think all dumb blondes are females. That is one dull dude."

Shapiro was figuring how to give the demonstration "focus," as he liked to say. "Cream, this is serious. It's gotta have a purpose, something. We have to have a list of demands, I mean a way to end it and get something out of it."

The Supreme Cream was told to find Roger and bring him back so that a set of demands against the Administration could be drawn up. On the roof of the car were new sounds. A PA system was being rigged and the vehicle converted into a rostrum. The steel above Shapiro buckled a little under the weight of the people, so he slid onto the floor, waiting to see how far the roof would cave in. The car shifted slightly and seemed to be lowering itself—the air was being let out of its tires. The feeling Shapiro got was of a bathysphere reaching the sea floor. Out the window were the fish talking, talking to each other in sonar. Not his species. Swim with the friendly fish in the revolutionary sea, swim if you can, pushed along by their noses. Ellie

Rector is a dolphin. She talks in helpful clicks. "You all right? D'you want anything?" Che in the high grass, behind rocks, in the forest, camping in dry ravines, he never got down to the sea. Shapiro, boy and man, revolutionary and reformer, went down to the bottom of the sea in a Sparkle toothpaste tube contraption built by Sil, and, resting there, considered he hadn't done anything wrong, so they couldn't give him more than probation; the revolution would be over when he had to take a crap, for then they'd haul him up and, "Officer, dean, you wouldn't refuse a toilet bowl to a young revolutionary, your own student, too, who trusts your justice because he's innocent and hasn't done anything wrong."

The Supreme Cream returned with Roger. Both of them pushed their heads in the window and, surprisingly, Roger readily agreed to the demands suggested by Shapiro: (1) Amnesty for the Norman Thomas Five, (2) abolition of Regulation XXVII, (3) a joint faculty-student-Administration committee with final authority for discipline, and (4) a new Regulation XXVIII guaranteeing complete freedom of speech and assembly on the campus. Within hours, they became known as the Four Points.

Night had come on when the Four Points were given to the world by Roger Elias, who stood in a slight crouch on the top of the sunken police car, his forearms raised and his fingers hooked in a gesticulation that made him look as though he were going to disfigure his face, scratch his flesh out of passion. It was a misplaced, overly intense oratorical style for the moment. It was Roger's only style, taunting, eloquently insulting, but misapplied on a crowd that was softly sitting, would not leave, and wanted no action.

"A night for Baez," the fattish, Protestant chaplain, Roysterman, wrote on one of the disorganized pieces of paper which he hoped to make into a book or an article. "I wish Joan had been singing on top of the police car. It was a night for her soft guitar. Like the night of the candles in Chicago." But it was not like the night of the candles in Chicago, at the 1968 Democratic National Convention, the college students beaten away by the police but coming back gentle. That had been a night of youth made tender by the violence done them.

This was a different night. The young people didn't expect to be forcibly dislodged; even strict institutions allow a degree of blockage, and the University was mild. No one expected the University to do anything, so there was no tension. The minister misinterpreted what he came upon, but it is hard to be a priest. Roysterman's God had left his tabernacle; the minister had to look for Him among the hosts, as he had in Washington at the reflecting pool in 1963, at Brown's Chapel in Selma, at the walls of the Pentagon, in Chicago—wherever a spirit moved through the people the man came to find God. "Boy, is there a God in history!" he'd exclaim to his wife, who had no faith but hard morals. "There's no other God." He drank too much; he'd had a couple of low affairs with college girls going through the ecstatic religious deceptions that mark the end of some people's childhoods; he was self-dramatizing, a touch paranoid, but a believer.

"Everything all right?" he asked through the car window, and then stood around for the next hour talking to the two campus guards. The boys who'd been at them earlier had moved off under the disapproval of the other students and now Roysterman, who had to devise a function for himself, a "relevant role" in his language, began little consultations with Roger, the Supreme Cream, Ellie, and the half-dozen other principals, asking if they didn't think the guards were a provocation. Some thought yes, some thought no, but in one part of the minister's Verbal History Project transcript it reads, "It was obvious to someone who'd been part of the non-violent movement that the continued presence of the campus security guards could be a source of trouble. The student leaders were concerned because they didn't want it blamed on them. Throughout it all I considered I had a triple role, one that was mediative, prophetic, and interpretive. I spent much time with the students and pushed them to clarify what they were saying, and I was struck by their sharp understanding of just where they were. They always knew what the total, evolving situation was. It was out of their concern that I undertook to persuade the policemen to leave, and I succeeded, which I thought was a good sign. I think they made a mistake in coming back . . . of course, they didn't do that for several hours. During that time Ray Shapiro was free to go, and I believe if they'd continued to stay away Shapiro would have left and all the rest, too. I stayed there until the police returned. This time there were four of them, I recall, maybe even six, not more, certainly not enough to indicate a build-up of force, but I got worried, because, mind you, during this time there hadn't been a move from the Administration. Nobody. No McVey, McTavish, just no one. The lights were out in Rennecker except for the ground floor where they were sitting in, so nobody was there, obviously. That caused me to go to Fletcher, but it was locked up, too. Absolutely unbelievable. The Administration had gone home to bed as far as I could see, leaving eight hundred or a thousand kids sitting-out and sitting-in, a police car captured, and a prisoner. I called McVey at home to make the Four Points known to the Administration. I reached McVey and he was very short. He said he wasn't interested in hearing anybody's demands, that it was a matter for Dean Pomfret.

"I called the other men in the chaplaincy, from the two other faiths, you know. They were very worried. We don't work for the University directly. We have an ecumenical board—it's businessmen and denominational execs—the religious establishment. Even before this happened, I don't think they were too happy with us. All three of us felt we should be with the kids, but there was the possibility our board wouldn't like it. Possibility did I say? It was a sure thing. That night we stood shifts. I took the first one, and actually, till about ten o'clock the next morning, the three of us were the only representatives of anything on the scene. No one from the Administration ever showed. No, I take that back, Yaldell was there, but he didn't do anything. Social structures have no idea how to respond to the pressure for change or even recognize it."

Roysterman could recognize it, even when it wasn't there. He needed these moments to feel God, and he needed them because each one was a new beginning. He sought out confrontational upheaval the way bankrupts once conspired to bring off the revolution which would abolish their debts. He had rushed to Selma, one of the first ones, weeks before King had put out the call, rushed away from an asbestos-shingled congregation of aging, outnumbered Protestants in Catholic South Buffalo, run off at the first chance from a fixed life of dismaying boredom among people who deeply appreciated it when the minister came to visit. From his church study, where he counseled on days there was someone to counsel, he could see the stationary dust cloud over the steel mills and the bell tower of St. Rose of Lima, which he hated and envied. So many people there in the Catholic congregation they had eleven masses on Sundays. Sometimes he put on his almost-black suit and his clerical collar to walk the streets and hear people say, "Hello, Father." There were afternoons when he thought he could hear the spiders making webs on his church ceiling. Leaving his wife to tell the church Elders, he rushed to Selma where the motions of people, their compactness in the cause gave him spiritual adrenalin and where he made a minor place for himself. "Oh yes, Reverend Roysterman, good to see you again, yes, it is, Reverend Roysterman," King would say. He liked the feeling of calling Roysterman's name, good rollable syllables, so he remembered the fattish minister from Buffalo when he'd come to Selma during the weeks of building up and jabbing at Sheriff Clark to get him worked up enough for a mass clobbering that would bring on a crisis.

It was a bad time for the movement but a good time for Roysterman. Every day he marched to the county courthouse, and his morale held up even when the numbers were few and the marchers just youngsters because the old people had given up. He believed King's assistants when, every night, they preached in the church that they would get Congress to pass a new voting law; but it didn't matter as much as that he was there, with a place to sleep in a black family's living room and a position in the loose organization of things. He helped in the feeding of the volunteer pilgrims and worked in the office getting them housed, and took joy in their nervous disorientation when they arrived and in the disintegration of those who stayed any length of time. Their position in the world outside of Selma didn't count; they had no function but to be bodies. The roles they played in other places as social workers, teachers, lawyers, theologians, mothers weren't included in that drama. They were inconsequential as individuals in Selma, good only for standing for hours by the rope which the police wouldn't let them pass. The important people had no time to see them. They even had to wait to see Roysterman, who was interviewed several times by a radio reporter from Cleveland and a non-commercial FM station in New England. He wrote his only published article during Selma, a firsthand account for a church publication.

Roysterman's letdown after Selma was awful. For a few days he had some celebrity to cushion re-entry into South Buffalo. A few churches asked him to come to speak; there was a lecture at a small college and an invitation to be on one of those radio shows where any drunk with a dime can call up and tell you you're a nigger-lover right on the air. One did, but it wasn't pleasing because the spiders were preparing silky trampolines on the church ceiling. By rights the congregation should have fired him for running away like that—not so much as arranging for a substitute—but they were only confused. Medical missionaries who had returned to the States to raise funds for Uganda X-ray machines appeared to think Selma was an acceptable form of alternative service to God, as did the denominational magazine and the President of the United States.

Roysterman was not looking for martyrdom, but he was disappointed the congregation didn't sack him, because it would have gotten him out of South Buffalo. Instead, he grew a beard and spent his time with the amateur left in hooky demonstrations, hoping God would come out from behind his cloud and inspirit him either to love his parishioners or leave them. And he looked for Selma again, but Selma was special; it had lasted a long time. The Pentagon was barely a day and a half and Chicago less than a week.

Anti-social morbidities tweaked him. He protested against the war, but he wanted it to go on forever; he protested racial injustice, and was content to see it perpetuated. He lived not for the triumph of the revolution but for its permanent prolongation, for the sight of God it provided, for the camaraderie, the new man it made of him. He supported any cause that would spread revolt, defiance, disorganization, picked up and spread every possibility of disaster— atomic radiation, population explosion, famine—prayed that every proposal for the solution of man's problems, from vitamins to irrigation, would fail. He hated computers out of fear they were as good as their makers said they were. His God was held in being by contention with evil.

He climbed out of South Buffalo by wangling a change

of venue to the campus, and on this night he thrust himself forward as intermediary and interpreter, the go-between in his second Selma. It was a part he had trouble making people accept. He would be asked to speak at some of the meetings by the students and let in on some of their strategy, but like the first Selma, he often was inventing functions for himself. The Administration started off chary of him and ended regarding him as one of the enemy.

People brought sandwiches and sleeping bags. Marshmallows were toasted over small fires, and the few who'd been at the Pentagon told of doing the same there at night, after the teargassing and the skirmishing, toasting marshmallows, drinking a little wine, smoking a little pot, and a defiant fuck that maybe the soldiers saw—love act on the night grass or a last attempt to make somebody react and do something. People listened and wondered if it were true, what they said they did, and was it a right thing to do, revolutionary or disgusting, demeaning the cause, demeaning love, just absurdly ridiculous? Is that our generation? The now generation. Is that us? Half the population is under twenty-five, but half of them are under twelve.

Few people slept in the bags. The speechmaking was almost continuous but the listening spotty. Roger and three or four of the young men closest to him Indian-trotted in the recrossing, incomprehensible pattern of ants, meeting every so often and getting up close to each other to whisper and then Indian-trot away toward darkened buildings, dorms, or the streets outside. The Supreme Cream stayed with Shapiro, who went through a period of wisecracking out the car window, and several periods of sending the beautiful boy off to bring Roger over so they could argue. For a while Shapiro slumped, unhappy with himself that he should care if they threw him out of school. No place else would take him; the blackball system in higher education is foolproof—you can't get in the next school without your records from the last.

No one had anything for Ellie Rector to do. She knew she was tired, but she wouldn't leave. Staying on the outside and listening in glimpses between shoulders, she moved around the conversational groups. One girl was talking about women's rights, saying women were the most niggerized people in all America, the real step-an'-fetch-its, even now in the revolution. The men were doing the speaking and the deciding and the girls were running for coffee, sandwiches, and pillows. Ellie thought about that, turning over the fact that she was between boy friends, the first time something important was happening that no deep voice was leaning down to explain it to her. The thought induced no liberated exaltation, merely a sense of incompleteness. Maybe she was niggerized, but what could she do? They don't have a chant like "black is beautiful" for girls. How did that girl get un-niggerized? Maybe she wasn't.

Her boy friends had not been quite the insipid types suggested by the remarks of the admission counselor in her file, but they hadn't been like these boys. She'd never met any young men like them. Apart from their maleness, their exaggeration and their involvement were almost unbelieve-able and therefore compelling. She'd dated dedicated athletes, hard-working med students, men from law school with enthusiasm for their profession, but they weren't compa-rable, except maybe Shapiro, but not even he . . . his careful misgiving, his worrying, his reworking, his obsessive concern with doing right and being right. The Supreme Cream, in face and body, on screen or television tube, he was the most ideally beautiful male she had seen, which was why Sil had given him the name.

Of all, Sil was the most interesting because he was the most foreign. Not one thing about him could Ellie recog-nize in herself, her father, or in anybody she'd known at all well. He was new. Monique, his girl, Slob Child, the dirtier and uglier she was and the worse she acted, the prouder Sil got and pushed her forward to be admired. Ellie had seen her squat on a fire hydrant and pee. So had any of the crowd who might have been looking.

The Supermarket Is a Boon to Mankind stayed the night. They were off by themselves and Ellie, thinking, wandered into the center of their circle. "Who are you fellas? Friends of Sil's?" she asked.

WAR GERM: I'm a bacterium, and I bite little asses.

FILTER TIPS: I'm the bad chromosome.

ELLIE: I mean, are you students or one of the—

SPARKLE TOOTHPASTE TUBE: One of the, one of the, one of the. We're one of nothing. You're one of the what? What are you one of?

ELLIE: I guess I'm one of what they've been calling the Norman Thomas Five.

TEAR: One of the five. That's pretty good. Are you one of your father's children?

ELLIE: One of four.

TEAR: That's better. One of four. And you're one of the students.

WAR GERM: One of twenty-five thousand. Bite her ass.

ELLIE: I'm a girl, so I guess that makes me—

WAR GERM: It doesn't make you at all. It means two more bites. You're one of billions.

FILTER TIPS: Have you ever been one of the one?

ELLIE: One of the one what?

SPARKLE TOOTHPASTE TUBE: One of one you.

"I'm too tired for this," Ellie shouted. The war germ made a motion as if to bite, but Ellie ran away, going to her room where she fell into bed without undressing or brushing her teeth. It was after ten when she woke the next morning with a feeling that the Slob Child had come to her with a message in a dream. She couldn't remember what, and she had no time to try. She'd be late for class, but that was crazy, too, going to class as if they all weren't still sitting out there in front of Rennecker. She'd always gone to class. She could go to class and then go to Rennecker. That would be disloyal. She could go to class and insist they discuss the sit-in. Last night one of the speakers—well, *everybody* is a one of something more than one, isn't she? he?—they?—one of the speakers suggested that people go to classes and demand that the sit-in be discussed. Ellie decided she would not know how to do that, so she had better cut.

At Rennecker the situation had turned tight. Greeks, jocks, and unaffiliated anti-radicals were piling up on one side of the crowd, heckling the speaker on top of the car and working up to something more direct. Yaldell was there trying to calm them, as were several faculty and another lower-echelon person from the Administration. The windows of Rennecker were again filled with the clerical staff, watching as it began to worsen. The difficulty in a school the size of the University is that it's pure happenstance if a faculty member who knows a student and presumably has some influence with him comes when he's needed.

"I think I want to go in there to the bursar's office," one of the antis declared in his loudest, most artificial voice. He was prepped for action.

His buddy picked up the idea and said, just as loudly, "I have to go in there and see my shrink. I need counseling very badly. I'm a victim of aggressive and hostile feelings whenever I see large groups of people sitting down in front of doorways."

"The hell with that," said a third, who was past play-acting. "I'm sick, sick, sick of this crud and their protests. They're not the only ones who go to the school. We pay our money, and I'm going into that building and kick the ass of anybody who tries to stop me."

About a score moved forward, stepping on the hands of as many seated people as they could, so that by the time they got to the entrance a fist fight had started. It brought the demonstrators to their feet, Shapiro almost out of the car, and Yaldell and five or six campus security people running to break it up. The Greeks, jocks, and unaffiliated antis retreated, rejoining their group off to the side.

The jeering went on, the people piled up to take sides or just watch as the institution began to unfasten, turn away from its ordinary occupations, and ignore the little customs and ways that make it possible for thousands of people to cooperate with each other. Throughout the night, care had been taken to protect the flower gardens in front of Rennecker from inattentive feet. Now they were stepped on and damaged. People stopped using the wire trash baskets.

The hours of the morning were used up with as many as a thousand people waiting for an event of some kind. The initiative would surely come from the Administration; but by noon nothing had happened. Roger and his friends were up on the car roof monotonously demanding Pomfret's presence and the Four Points. There was nothing more they could do. Other and more radical tactics were argued, but there weren't enough troops. Less than half the people standing in and around Rennecker could properly be called protestors, and they were "unradicalized" liberals who thought what they were doing was enough. The Conservative Alliance and the student government leaders had already resigned from the demonstration, saying something that would be said ad infinitum in the days ahead: "While we are in full-hearted accord with the aims and purposes of this demonstration, we cannot accept the means. In the long run, it will do no one any good to gain one right by the destruction of another."

No reliable, complete account exists of what was happening at this time in the Administration. In the Verbal

History Project transcripts, Hungerford and McVey speak of being "consulted" and "apprised" of what was happening. McVey certainly understates his role, which he describes as minimal until the late afternoon meeting when an agreement was reached. McTavish and Pomfret admit they "looked at the situation somewhat differently," but both deny the two serious arguments which Yaldell says McTavish told him they had. Yaldell was outside trying to keep order all day long, so he was never present at any of the Administration discussions. He says, however, it was common knowledge that McTavish wanted to call the city police and end the whole thing with a fast blow, and Pomfret was for negotiating—he denies it—or at least for seeing whether the demonstrators could be talked into leaving.

The one person who was talking to most of the principals most of the day was Roysterman. Much of his story is disputed:

"After we broke up the fight with the shit-kickers—ha, it's not a nice name but that's what everybody ended up calling the jocks and the Greeks—well, anyway, after the fight, I decided it was a dangerous situation and we couldn't let it go on. I went into Rennecker Hall, found McTavish, and told him so. He said he agreed, and they were going to call the police. I told him that wouldn't solve anything, but if that was what he was going to do, I demanded to see Pomfret and tell him so. McTavish had the nerve to say he was chairing a meeting of the scholarship committee and couldn't be interrupted. I lost my temper. I'll admit that, and while I was letting McTavish know what I thought, Pomfret came along, and I gave it to him, too. He denied the Administration was going to use force, at least right then, but he said negotiations were out of the question, especially with a mob camping there and helping a prisoner to escape from campus security. 'Nobody's escaped. The prisoner's right where campus security put him, and as far as I know has no intention of going anywhere unless they tell him to.'—That's what I answered. Pomfret said he wished he could believe that, or he made some remark like that. And I told him, that's when I told him, 'Don't believe me, just tell the campus cops to go bring Shapiro in here, or wherever they want him, and you'll see no mob has freed any prisoner or anything like that.' Then, as I recall—remember, I didn't keep notes—Pomfret said, 'If that's true, I'll have him brought in and we can all sit down and talk.' "

As this was going on in Rennecker, other pressures were building. Mirsky and the astronomer stopped by McVey's office after lunch, because in the Faculty Club dining room the social scientist had said, "Maybe, it could be, yes, could very definitely be," when his friend had asked if this was it. They hadn't seen McVey, but they'd run into other faculty who were also concerned that something be done. McVey's secretary hinted that a lot of people had come in with a lot of suggestions, the one constant being that the worst possible course would be to allow things to drag on unresolved.

In the early afternoon, Pomfret asked campus security to bring Shapiro into Rennecker. This was done without any difficulty, perhaps because Roger wasn't aware of what they were doing until he caught up with the officers and Shapiro inside the lobby of the building. He screamed, "The Four Points! Remember, nothing but the Four Points!" Shapiro appeared to nod yes and was guided upstairs. Roysterman, who went with Shapiro, recalled, "Shapiro immediately told Pomfret that negotiations would have to be on the Four Points, and then McTavish broke in and said the Administration wasn't about to negotiate anything, that Shapiro, SDS, Elias, and the rest didn't represent the student body, and that probably half the people in the demonstration were non-students. Pomfret was much calmer, but he said there couldn't be any discussion while people were trying to coerce the University, especially while the police car was being held. Then I remember Shapiro wanted to trade himself for the police car so that talk could begin. Pomfret answered he didn't think that was possible, since there were charges against Shapiro. That's when I said that I'd seen the whole thing and that campus security had arrested the wrong boy."

INTERVIEWER: But you hadn't gotten there until the fight at the door was over and Shapiro was already in the car.

ROYSTERMAN: Yes, but I talked to some reliable witnesses. What I said was meant to be a way for the Administration to save face and at the same time establish a precedent of negotiations with the student body.

INTERVIEWER: Is that what Pomfret understood, that he was setting a precedent?

ROYSTERMAN: I don't know what he understood, but it did. Pomfret said that in that case holding Shapiro had been a misunderstanding, and Shapiro went downstairs, got up on the car, and this is almost verbatim, he shouted, "It's a swap! Me for the police car, and the Administration'll negotiate." There was negative discussion between the kids about the deal, but they decided to go for it.

INTERVIEWER: What kind of negative discussion?

ROYSTERMAN: Well, I'd rather not discuss that. Ask them about it.

As Shapiro set forth the terms, Roger began to shout, accusing him of having traded away "our power lever—you and the car. What the hell are we going to bargain with now?"

Shapiro gave a few scratches of the head, feeble ones for he was tired and shaky. "We're still sitting-in. We've got that to bargain with. They're more concerned about that than a car with four flat tires and a bent roof."

"You've given away our whole goddamn position. It's a sellout."

"I was there and you weren't, and don't talk to me like that. I'm just as tired as you and it's just as hard for me as it is for you, so don't talk to me like that. You come in there and do the negotiating if you think you can do better," Shapiro came back, shaking.

Roger did another tirade. He was a thin young man, and when he went into his forensic rages he seemed to strip himself of skin so that he looked like one of those plastic anatomy models, a creature of white wire nerves, striped muscles, and red and blue veins, an elongated, straining madman, but Shapiro could look at him, and after hearing him out two or three times, could shrug.

"Not me, not me in your cop-out negotiations. I'm with the movement," said Roger.

"Okay, not you," Shapiro said, and a committee of Roger's adherents, the Supreme Cream, and Shapiro himself went back into Rennecker to negotiate. Roysterman stayed with them, step by step.

"I received a telephone call from Dean Pomfret informing me that the police car had been released and that there was a representative group, a committee from the demonstrators who wanted to discuss the situation," McVey says in his Verbal History transcript. "Subsequently, it was said by some people that we negotiated under duress. We didn't. I want to make this point very clear. The car had been released. Dean Pomfret was satisfied that Ray Shapiro had not tried to escape and that his detention had been an error. There were only a few sit-inners inside Rennecker Hall. Most of them were outside, so that we weren't under pressure.

"Then, this is a university. The rules that apply for dealing with the Soviet Union should not be applicable in talking to the students. Later, I think many of us learned there were some students who looked at the University as a foreign power against which any tactic was licit, but that approach is the end of education. Then, too, we were very concerned about the fighting that had already taken place between members of the student body. This is a very bad thing, and we were worried that it might happen again. If a conversation, or many conversations, could end the sit-in with all its built-in potential for trouble, I think we were bound to try. Subsequently, some people have criticized us and said we should have used the police that day. I'm not so sure, even now, with the virtue of hindsight. Bringing in the police should be the utter last resort of a school administration, and at that hour on that day we had not tried everything short of physical force. People who urge the use of the police in these situations forget that there can be violence—it matters not who starts it—but people can be injured; the resulting bitterness is incalculable, and then what do we do as an educational institution—not a nation, or a sovereign power, but a school? Do we ask everyone to walk into classes the next day and resume where they left off? Violence, I don't care how justified, has no place in the pedagogical process; it's the antithesis of it, and we, as educators, were not going to be the ones who introduced it on this campus. The coercion, the violence, the use of every form of compulsion at their power was begun here by Mr. Elias and his associates in the SDS. Ultimately we had to respond, but always at the lowest possible level."

McVey then goes on to relate his version of the talks, repeating that they were not negotiations, that it was impossible for any detached person to call the outcome a capitulation or an SDS victory. The chancellor's position was that the Four Points were essentially three—amnesty, a new disciplinary procedure for students, and changing Regulation XXVII. He disposed of amnesty for the Norman

Thomas Five by pointing out that since they had not been charged with anything the furor was gratuitous. On the other two questions, he said he would recommend to the president that committees, with student representation on both, be appointed to study the problems and make recommendations. He also promised to support the committee's findings.

"VICTORY!!!" Roysterman bellowed into the microphone from the car roof with such force he induced a squeaking, screaling bolt of feedback. "VICTORY! VICTORY! victory!" he hollered in a fatty glow of excitement. Afterward he explained that he got to the microphone first because Shapiro was so tired that he was dangerously slow in getting back from Fletcher Hall where the meeting with McVey and Pomfret had taken place. The danger, Roysterman said, was that the jocks and the Greeks would begin another attack before the demonstrators could hear the news and disperse. Thus it was that Roysterman's version of "the agreement," as he called it, was the first version the campus heard; the other versions never caught up with his. He thereby almost singlehandedly created future misunderstandings and disappointments and an awakening and hardening of attitudes among people who hadn't given the controversy any thought except to glance at it and call it an unimportant, squalid, little typically SDS mess. But now, if SDS had a victory, victory, victory, the Administration must have had a defeat.

The Roysterman version had McVey granting amnesty and creating two committees to rewrite Regulation XXVII, as per the Four Points, and to take away disciplinary authority from the Administration and give it finally and completely to a joint faculty-student-Administration tribunal. Yaldell heard and wouldn't believe. He was standing with a bunch of the antis whom he'd been keeping tranquilized for hours by reiterating the sentence, "Let the proper people handle it." The boys around him now gave it back to him.

"Let the proper people handle it, Mr. Yaldell?"

"Is that what you call handling it?"

"Why stop there? Just give them the place."

Yaldell was wondering what language might convince them now that the proper people knew what they were doing, when he was interrupted by a proper-looking man who, however, was not one of the proper people. "Have you seen the tear from the eye of weeping mankind?" the assistant curator of the DuPont Museum inquired.

"Yeah, right here," he was told by a shit-kicker, who put a stubby index finger tip to the tender skin under one of his eyes and pulled down so the organ bulged and showed its little red blood vessels.

Roger reacted predictably. "Fink-out, cop-out, sell-out! Shit, Shapiro, how could you? My God, did he give a speech about how change must proceed through 'incremental augmentations' and the need to use 'amelioristic models'? Did he give you all the bullshit?"

"I got the best we could get. There wasn't anything else to settle for. Think a minute, will you, Roger? Just once, as a personal favor to the guy you spend all your energy dumping on, think a minute. One minute," Shapiro asked, while a hand started scalpward for a little reassuring scratch, but it was too tired and fell back to his side.

"Shapiro, I keep telling you, I've told you so often: YOU THINK LIKE THEY DO! You weren't in there to make the best deal according to their circumstances. Don't tell me McVey doesn't have the power to change XXVII. Don't tell me all he can do is recommend. You weren't there to be a big, responsible, liberal, establishment statesman. You were there to make a REVOLUTION."

"Roger, you think tactically for a minute yourself. I had to settle for a victory. What if I'd come out of there and said they didn't go for it, so we continue to sit. How many people do you think would stick? Once we got amnesty, the emotional issue was over. XXVII is an abstraction. They'd never sit for it. We had no troops, Roger," Shapiro countered.

Roger lowered himself onto the police car, which had not yet been towed away. His feet were still on the ground, but the rest of him was lying head down on the car, listening to Shapiro. Then he turned and was fully on his feet again, accusing, nagging, "And who gave away amnesty? You did, Shapiro. You gave away our gut, emotional issue, and then you give away our free speech issue, because you've already given away our gut issue. Weeks we work to build up this thing, and whang, bang, bong, the great radical theoretician, Shapiro, who can always demonstrate the time isn't right, gives away our issue. Shapiro, I want my issue back."

"Pardon me, but have either of you seen the tear from the eye of weeping mankind?"

"It's up my ass and I'm using it, so fuck off, will ya? Can't you see we're talking?" Roger said to the curator, who did as he was ordered, going away and inquiring until he asked Myron Mirsky, who smiled and said softly, "Everywhere and all the time."

"Have *you* seen the tear from the eye of weeping mankind?" he asked Ellie Rector.

"Oh, isn't it beautiful? I saw it a little while ago. I don't know where it is now," she told the proper man. He thanked her and meandered farther till he bumped into the Supreme Cream.

"Haven't seen it in the last hour," the Cream said.

"Do you know the name of the boy who has it?"

"No, but he's a Fuckhead."

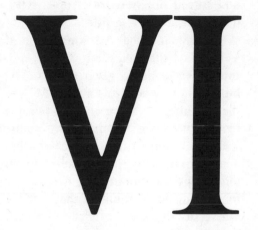

VI

THE NEXT FEW DAYS saw the University in controversy without crisis. Because the Administration took a day and a half to get out a mimeographed statement, the *Daily Review* went with the Roysterman version of the agreement under a headline that read, U, A.A. BACK DOWN—SDS WINS. There were letters to the editor, discussions on the University radio station, and an inflammatory speech by Roger Elias under the Minerva to a large crowd which had come out to see the teaching assistant from math who made the University and A. A. McVey back down. His peroration ended with the statement: "Next time we'll really put the motherfuckers up against the wall!"

The chancellor seemed to be moved by urgent premonitions. Instead of proceeding by the customary intervals of months, he announced the Administration would go ahead with the creation of the two committees immediately. But a worse crisis diverted everybody's attention so thoroughly the two committees never met. This unlucky *deus ex machina* broadened the area of conflict, split the faculty, and forced hundreds of people, who up to then had been indifferent, to choose sides.

McVey and the Administration did not respond to it as they had the police car. They were shaken and did everything they could to get it settled. They couldn't. "The Administration made mistakes," McVey said, in defense of their failure. "We know that, but I wish that some of the faculty who are so quick to point them out had been willing to help us during the months we tried to work out a just solution to the Russell difficulty. I won't embarrass anyone by mentioning the names of people we approached to serve on the committee that was trying to find a solution. University faculties everywhere criticize their administrations, but they won't take on the responsibilities of administration themselves."

"What committee?" one history professor asked when he heard McVey make the statement on a radio program. "The reason the thing kicked around so long was because the Administration thought they could bureaucratize it to death, shift it around from office to office and avoid it. There never was a committee or person or anything that took the responsibility for dealing with it head on."

The contradictions and recriminations were as murky as Eldon Russell, Jr., was flamboyant, delineated by his cocky intellectuality, his histrionics, and his immovable belief in the correctness of his opinions. He grew up in suburban Detroit, but that didn't stick on him; he chose instead to model himself on the English university don of a past era. He always wore an academic gown, and he was the only full professor at the University without a doctorate, limiting himself to the M.A. in the style of famous scholars at the old universities. His field was classical antiquity, Greek particularly; he held appointments in history and archaeology, made excellent translations of Greek writers, wrote many books, and was considered outstanding, one of the best.

Eldon Russell, Jr., looked down on the modern research drudge (his expression) who avoided undergraduate teaching. Russell loved it, and he continued to do it years after his standing as a scholar would have exempted him. Undergraduates loved him. His lectures were the kind of drama that alumni remembered when they had forgotten the names of their other teachers. Russell's most famous undergraduate course, *The Foundations of Western Civilization*, had to be held in an amphitheater seating a thousand students, and even then there were people who wanted to register for it and couldn't get in.

Eldon Russell, Jr., admired Western civilization—"and that's only to be expected," a non-admiring colleague once remarked, "it produced Eldon Russell, Jr., didn't it?" To Russell it was incomparably preferable to any other civilization. He gave the others their due, but when he said the word "Hindu" he made it sound like some scabrous dermatitis you'd catch by dipping into the Ganges. "The Japanese," he would say, "have become a great nation because they are learning to put their art and culture within a Western frame." He talked about "undeveloped" countries, preliterate societies, and sometimes said "barbarian" and "savage" in his lectures when referring to people who were not white.

Some students, black and white, began to complain about these eccentricities, but Russell's reply was, "I have my credentials. As an undergraduate I helped integrate the college barber shop. In 1963 I went to Washington to march behind Dr. King's banner. I revered Dr. King as a man, as a black man, and as a great Christian leader. He didn't have to concoct an overblown bedtime story about his family's origins in the tropical rain forests; he was able to be a Christian minister and a fully developed man of immense self-confidence and poise without needing to identify with some animalist, fetish priest of the Upper Volta. I am a complete assimilationist. I believe the black man's only future in America is the same as the white man's. Both of them must carry on in the genius of Western civilization, and note I didn't say white civilization, I said Western, a civilization to which black men have contributed, though not so much as white, but that's pure happenstance."

As the civil rights movement died and gave way to the strident affirmations of black unity, black separation, black power, beauty, and goodness, Russell stayed the same. The animus against him didn't. It grew, until finally the Student Afro Association passed a resolution calling him "an institutional racist." It was printed in the *Daily Review* and shoved into the hands of white people, who looked confused and asked, "Well, what do they want?" It read:

Professor Russell thinks the biggest favor he can do for the black man is to make him into a Western-civilized white man like Professor Russell. He cannot believe a black man can be civilized in a black way or a yellow man in a yellow way. So the black students who come to this University every year hear one of its most famous professors say, "You ain't nuthin' till we wash the black out of you and give you a white man's soul." White students come and they hear the same professor tell them, "You ain't got nuthin' to worry about, you're the tops, and the only way the rest of 'em can be the tops is to do jus' like you."

This is institutional racism. We don't think Professor Russell is a bigot. He is just as snotty to the white students—maybe even a little more—as to black ones who come up to him after class. But he is perpetuating everything that has kept the black down. He is keeping up the idea that the black man never had his own thing which he did well, that he never had anything to give other people, that all he ever contributed to America "is a freer use of the pelvis in social dancing."

The University Student Afro Association does not believe a course in Western civilization should be taught any more. That day is over, but if it is taught it should be taught by somebody who doesn't believe that it was a few white Europeans who made it for everybody on this globe. Somebody else should teach this course, if it has to be taught at all, but if the University wants to keep him teaching it, then there should be somebody who is given time in Professor Russell's course to answer him.

For a year, the Student Afro Association pushed its protest with McVey, who sent the blacks to the Dean of Arts and Sciences, who sent them to the Dean of the College, who sent them to the Committee on Curriculum, which sent them to the All-University Committee on Human Rights and Relations, which sent them to the chairman of the history department, who set up an "informal" committee with the chairman of the archaeology department, which decided the best thing it could do was to send them back to McVey. After a year of this the Student Afro Association resolved on action. Conceivably it might have been delayed by its faculty adviser, a young social anthropologist, but he took the position that "They didn't ask me what I thought they should do, and I don't give advice unless I'm asked."

Early one afternoon the blacks seized Ripon Hall, a small building used mostly for undergraduate classes, but which also housed the chairman of the history department. He was bagged along with his secretary. All the other non-blacks in the building were expelled by members of the SAA, who walked into the classrooms and announced to teachers and students that class was dismissed. The non-black reaction was submissive. People packed up their books, gathered coats and papers, and left, as though they had been told there was a fire drill. The only near fight was between two blacks.

"Man, don't call me Uncle Tom. I came to this University to learn, not for this shit," the young man said, getting up from his desk. He turned and looked at the class instructor, who was stuffing his briefcase, and told him, "Mr. Parsons, don't do that. Don't stop the class. Don't listen to these people. They don't talk for the black man—not this black man." Mr. Parsons continued his preparations to leave. "Mr. Parsons, you got rights, too. So do these other students."

"They've done a real fine dye job on your brain, brother, made you all white," the SAA member told the boy.

"Aww, don't gimme that shit, man. I grew up somewheres just like the place you did. Only difference is when I read about some cat in the papers running around with a natural and a tiger-tooth necklace I laugh and say, that's great for the Johnny Carson show. I don't need that to know black is beautiful. I know that. I learned that already. I came here to get an education, which is what I need now."

"Baby," the militant student warned him, "You'd better get your shit together."

Realizing he was exchanging stock phrases in a debate they'd both heard before, the black student turned back to the instructor: "Please, Mr. Parsons, don't go. Don't do like they say. Man, don't you see if you do there's never gonna be an end to this shit?"

Mr. Parsons wasn't having any, so the non-white student left with the non-blacks, congregating outside the main entrance, muttering to himself, "Aww hell, damn and double hell, old-fashioned, dried-out, broken-down hell, hell, hell and triple it." He sat down on a piece of grass and just about wept.

Inside the building the captors went to work, using file cabinets, desks, chairs, and dismantled bookcases to barricade the first-floor windows and doors. A sign appeared below the ledge of a second-floor windowsill reading, FREDERICK DOUGLASS UNIVERSITY—NO WHITES NEED APPLY. And then nothing happened. No noise, no heads looking out windows. The building looked as disused as it did during intersession. The students who had been kicked out were unable to react. They congregated by the entrance, whispering or talking in low voices, looking at each other for cues.

"A group of them came into my office, the outer office. I was talking to my secretary," the chairman of the history department related to the Verbal History Project. "I think it was—yes, as I recall, Tully Haskins was doing the talking, but I don't recall that other boy, the one they call B. J. He wasn't with them. They said—oh, I can't remember exactly how they put it. It was a pretty upsetting experience. You didn't know what to expect. The gist of it was that they had taken over the building and were going to keep it. I can't remember—no, they didn't tell us they'd evicted everybody else, or I think I'd have been even more upset. They said something like, 'You two'—meaning me and Miss Cutler, my secretary—'are going to have to stay here until we iron out the Eldon Russell business.' Yes, I think that's how it went. I'm sure it is, because I remember now, just shortly after that, I called Chancellor McVey to tell him, and he was the one who told me they'd evicted everyone else. I suppose up to then he hadn't known we were still there. I was nervous when Haskins, or whoever it was, said that, but I do recall I told them I would not discuss anything under duress, that they should leave my office at once. Well, you know, they did. I wonder what I would have said if I'd known that Miss Cutler and I were alone in the building. Before they left they said they'd been trying for a year to do something about Eldon's course without force. I remember feeling a little ashamed when they said that, because they had, but my God, what did they expect me to do? There just wasn't anything anybody could do. That's why it got passed around that way.

"Put this on your tape. I never wanted to be the departmental chairman. They couldn't agree on two other men —never mind their names. I was a compromise candidate, and I took it with the explicit understanding that I wouldn't have to do anything. I'm not an administrator. Couple of years ago they wanted me to be dean of the graduate faculties. I refused. I've spent my life working on seventeenth- and eighteenth-century France and Germany. You might say I've lived more at Porte Royale than here in twentieth-century America. I'm not defending it. After something as terrible as all this, any sane man wonders if he's misapplied his life, spending years with a Leibniz or a Descartes. They were better men than we, though."

Thus the chairman, captive returnee from the Enlightenment.

Excerpts from the Verbal History Project:

MC VEY: That twenty-four-hour period commencing with the seizure of Ripon Hall is difficult to reconstruct. So many things happened. I first learned of the chairman of the history department's forcible detention from himself. We knew, of course, about the expulsion of everybody from the building, but when he called it was quite a shock, or, let's say it put a different light on the situation. There has been some criticism of us for not moving immediately with all necessary force, and this was an option we discussed. I decided against it for two reasons. I was terribly concerned about the safety of the chairman and his secretary.

We had no definite idea as to who was in that building—we'd been told there were non-students, but the people who told us couldn't be sure. I was not going to do anything precipitous. There was also the possibility of over-reaction. I was sensitive to this. There had been incidents from Harvard to UCLA of students detaining people for a few hours, and nothing much came of it. The black students at Columbia held a dean captive for nearly twenty-four hours, and it worked out all right. I mention this by way of rebuttal to those who have said the Administration was oblivious to the history and tactics of these things. Lastly, President Hungerford was at NYU giving a speech, and I preferred to await his return. Naturally, we talked on the phone.

The first thing we tried to do was to make contact with the people in Ripon Hall. I phoned the building, but I didn't get an answer. Then Dean Pomfret and Dean Robertson of the College went over there to see if they could talk to someone. They banged on the doors and got no answer. We discussed my going over with a bullhorn and talking up through the windows, but the people at the meeting decided, and I agreed, that wouldn't be wise. We were still discussing what we would do when a call came from Professor Myron Mirsky. He said he'd gotten a call from a student of his, a black student, who, he believed, was either in the building or had just left it. The student said that in one half-hour the Student Afro Association would hold a press conference at the entrance to Ripon Hall, where they would make their demands known, and from that conference some sort of communication between the SAA and us could begin. I called the history chairman and told him and asked him if he was all right. He said he was, and with that I decided to wait at least until the conference. . . . Yes, I had talked to the police. We made no decisions. I was keeping Chief Manfried up to date.

After hanging up the phone to McVey, Mirsky kept his hand on the receiver like one who would momentarily make another call. He didn't. His hand stayed where it was because he was heavy with thinking, making small atonements for his own conduct, his omissions as well as his commissions, thinking that he did love this University, that he must do something, that he was not equipped, that analysis and understanding seemed good only to explain what had already happened, not to guide what would, that the boy, the math TA, Elias, knew far better how to act. Some voice said to him, we should study these things, work out a set of conflict models and from them develop a corresponding set of scenarios; suppose the blacks in Ripon Hall, for example, assume that the Administration—Mirsky made a forced effort of the soul and cut short these computations. It was the first time in many years he had not allowed himself to follow a thought until it diminished into uncertainty. It was hard to turn away from speculation; the ideas he'd begun to toy with were scratching and pinching in storage cells of his brain. As he tried to calm down and freeze the excited particles of thought, he remembered the difficulty he'd had as a young man teaching himself to think. He remembered the distractions of women, sports, or pleasant idleness, and the work it had taken to discipline himself into the habit of staying with his thoughts; how, by gradual changes, he had begun, sometimes for only a few minutes in a day, to enjoy the life of the mind. He took his hand off the phone preparatory to getting up from his desk, now picturing himself as a foolish, inept, unprepared man, not the descendant of the warriors of Israel, ancient or modern, but of the weak and whining men from the ghettos of Eastern Europe. But he said aloud, "We were the ones with ethics." Then he put on his coat and walked to Ripon Hall.

"That's how you have to understand my role," he said in the Verbal History transcripts. "I knew I was a clown when it came to mixing into such things, but I have a sense for the preservation of valuable things. There was no question it was serious for the University now, so that's why I injected myself at this point. I had no practical hope of being the successful Machiavelli and manipulating everybody to a happy ending. I understand manipulating people. I've studied it long enough, but I can't do it. I expected to fail, not in a definite precise sense, but because you could feel how enormously strong all of this was. But a Jew like myself has a great respect for the preservation of valuable things. It's interesting that in the end I explain the part I played not as a social scientist or an intellectual or a professor, but from the first beginnings, from the continuity with my origins. But the man who's talking with so much self-examination, is he the professor or the Jew who makes me feel I must discuss my motivations before telling you what I did?"

Instead of a press conference, the scene at Ripon Hall that greeted Mirsky was a loud, inchoate confusion of radicals, Administration, antis, evictees, newsmen, faculty, the curious, and the concerned, as well as a pile-up of students and teachers who had been scheduled to use the building. The radicals and antis were chanting and counter-chanting at each other. From time to time an egg would splatter, there would be roars and yells, but no hand-to-hand fighting, perhaps because neither side was sure of its strength or because the crowd was too diluted with neutrals.

Many of the faculty members were moving through the crowd, identifying themselves and asking people to "help" by leaving the area. But the crowd continued to build in size and noise, while the press conference was delayed without explanation or apology. The building remained locked. No one was visible through the windows.

"Please, it would really help if you fellows didn't stand here. It just attracts larger crowds," faculty continued to say.

In return they got, "See, if you're white, pay tuition, and you're not a communist, you can't even stand on the grass. . . . Since I can't go to class, I thought I'd stand here and see if I can find out why."

The crowd quieted immediately as a barricade was taken down at one of the doors and Tully Haskins and B.J. came out. They didn't go far, just a few steps from their portal. B.J. said nothing. He kept his arms crossed and appeared to be there to make sure Tully kept to the script.

Tully kept to the minimum: "No questions. I'm going to read it and that's it. This is a statement by the membership of the University Student Afro Association and it says,

"The black man and the black woman are barely tolerated ghosts on this campus, which, by so-called slum clearance, is taking away the homes of black people. We have nothing at this University. There are almost no black people here. There are no black deans, no black people high up in the Administration, a few token black professors, and less than three hundred black students. The black student who comes here is downed. He is taught nothing about himself. He is made to take a class where, to pass, he has to say that a black man is a white man with funny-colored skin. He is not told about his heritage in America or Africa. He is not told anything about himself, except that he is really a savage and lucky to be brought here in chains and kept in poverty. That is what Professor Eldon Russell, Jr., says, and the rest of the University must agree with him, because they do not shut him up or counteract him in any way. To change this there are a list of things that have to be done around here:

"1. Professor Russell to stop teaching.

"2. Stop all so-called slum clearance immediately.

"3. Admit as many black students to the University as blacks in the percentage of the population.

"4. Teach courses for black people with black teachers.

We want courses in black history, black psychology, black politics, black sociology.

"5. We want black dorms and clubs to develop and enjoy Negritude like whites have theirs.

"Tomorrow will be Afro Day on this campus. The black community will come here to be part of a celebration of black art and culture. . . . That is all."

The two spokesmen climbed back through the portcullis, which was sealed up behind them. While Mirsky was still looking at the place in the wall where they'd re-entered their fort, the black student who had telephoned earlier came up and gave him a written copy of the statement. The professor said he would give it to the Administration, adding that, whatever the reaction in Fletcher Hall, these weren't things you said yes or no to. There would have to be talk, a system of communication; and there was the chairman and his secretary. The student made no clear answer. Mirsky thought he heard him say that he would or might telephone later. The student gave a fidget, mumbled something, and was gone, leaving Mirsky in the crowd, which had thinned out and quieted down. It was late afternoon.

The SAA announcement had thrown people's attention forward and, by supplying a schedule of events, had made the situation at Ripon seem less urgently in need of a climax. But at Fletcher Hall anxiety did not ease. Mirsky found McVey and the deans and University vice-presidents dominated by a variety of unhappy emotions. The chancellor himself was holding to a cautiously firm equilibrium, encouraging the others to demonstrate their own unflappability.

He studied the list of demands and then said, "We could talk, using this as a starting point, if they released the chairman." McVey's social understanding was based on negotiation and compromise. He didn't like to hear people talk about "the art of the possible"—it was a cliché and an oversimplification, but he believed it nonetheless. Some of the men in the room had been speculating about the students' alarming "nihilistic approach." McVey couldn't think of how to deal with nihilism; it was outside the circle of his life experience, suggesting the philosophical dementia of minor nineteenth-century authors whose works he'd been obliged to read as a student. The SAA statement smacked of the familiar pragmatism of dealing and swapping, yet the chairman was still unextricated, and these students were black, and blacks sometimes seemed to have a death-of-the-gods streak in them.

McVey had the kind of mind which groups the elements of a situation in orderly, tabular lists. Sometimes they would be two simple lists of contrary opposites—for and against—sometimes they were complicated and with special tables for shared characteristics or elements. A mind that broke things down according to a set of a priori rules in law, economics, political science—but this situation would not fit. He could not, for instance, decide how to label whoever was in Ripon Hall. Were they students, black students, blacks, students duped by non-students, militants, agitators, civil rights workers, part of the student body, the opposition, who? He thought to avoid definition by categorizing and asserting propositions, but this translated the ambiguities into new forms: Talks cannot begin until (or unless?) they (who they?) release our chairman, sailors, gunboat, reconnaisance airplane, chargé d'affaires, pilots. A national people (student body? approved student organization?) loses its moral standing among peace-loving states of the world (truth-seeking faculties and its fellow, university-approved student organizations?) when it resorts to force (unilateral action? irresponsible banditry? direct action and confrontational politics?) because the only true forum for settling disputes among undergraduates or sovereign states is the United Nations, Congress, the Academic Senate, or a scientifically conducted, random sample of all the above.

"The police department has a plan for rescuing the chairman," the chancellor said. "It has its risks, but Chief Manfried believes it will work, and we're running out of options."

"You don't think it would be worth waiting to see if the boy calls me back?" Mirsky inquired, trying his best not to sound as though he was urging a line of action, but discussing options. He wondered why they all—himself, too—preferred options to choices. "Wouldn't an attempt to rescue the chairman risk someone getting hurt?"

"It might, Professor Mirsky," the chancellor replied, sad faced.

Professor Mirsky. Professor Mirsky. McVey always addressed people with a fluid formality; he knew how to use titles without being stuffy. Professor Mirsky. Professor Mirsky looked at the chancellor, wondering what kind of a person he might be. Since his appointment he had been very popular with the liberal arts faculty, one of them, sympatico with scholarship, with their ways and prides and their pretty pettinesses, a counterweight to Martin Hungerford, whose background was industrial relations or labor relations or some other non-field where opinionated ignoramuses advanced themselves with presumption. Professor Mirsky regarded Chancellor McVey for a long moment and decided he was a good man on his way to being a tragic one.

"Chief Manfried's plan is to wait until very late, early in the morning. Presumably most of the crowd outside of Ripon Hall will have left. Then create a distraction in front of the building by assembling a large number of police officers there. In the meantime, a small group with a fire department snorkel ladder will go up to the second-floor window of the chairman's office and rescue him and his secretary," McVey said, and then added, "I hope you'll treat that as confidential."

Mirsky grunted affirmatively, but the expression on his face registered skepticism.

McTavish immediately said, "We've had reports that there

are firearms in the building. If the police rushed it head-on, the chances of someone being injured would be much greater."

"How reliable are the reports?" asked Mirsky. "I've been standing out in front of the building for several hours, and I couldn't see anything inside. As far as I could tell, all the first-floor windows are barricaded."

"The reports are rumors," Dean Pomfret said, as he gave McTavish a sideways look.

The conversation then began to repeat itself. Finally it was decided to try to reach several Negro city councilmen and get them to come to the campus to try to get into the building and talk to whomever was in there. Mirsky said he would go back to his office in hopes the student would call again. Outside of McVey's door he ran into a former student of his who was working as a well-bred young man in some ill-defined role for the chancellor. The young man was jittery and unhappy. He had come to think highly of McVey who, he said, was pushed by Hungerford to act sharply to make up for the lenient handling of the Rennecker Hall sit-in and the police car.

"Has Hungerford forgotten his campus is surrounded on three sides by a black ghetto with nearly four hundred thousand people in it? This isn't just a private matter between the University and a few students," Mirsky said.

"I know," the young man agreed.

"You know. I know. Doesn't Hungerford? He's the one that should know."

"He was pretty upset by the police car, and the *Daily Review* saying SDS had won. He and A.A. have had a couple of pretty rough meetings."

"What's the use of rehearsing last week's blunders? Tell them that, tell them that," Mirsky said, going down the corridor and out the main entrance of Fletcher, where he stood on the portico looking down the steps at Minerva, Mother of Knowledge, and past her down the second tier of steps in the

Square below. In the evening it was quiet, a tender night spot where the globe from the fancy cast-iron lamps, which had once burned gas, gave light to the leaves. As fine as anything of its kind in America, the unaltered beaux arts center of the campus, superior to Cleveland and on a par with the San Francisco Civic Center or the Boston Public Library, but softer because of the foliage. The moderns could laugh at it, but it had that Victorian intricacy and elegance. It wasn't pompous, or heavy, much more successful than the McKim, Mead, and White campus at Columbia. Mirsky walked down the steps where, from the bottom, he could look up at the Minerva and at Fletcher. Then, detouring past Ripon to check, he went back to his office and waited for the telephone call.

A call came, but it was from McVey's office saying that a Negro city councilman had gone to Ripon and gotten inside.

Good. Mirsky decided they would soon call and tell him they were going to release the chairman. "While I was sitting there, I attempted to construct the nihilistic scenario," the Verbal History Project has him saying, "but it didn't fit the known facts. Those men in Cleveland who trapped, baited, and gunned down the policemen, there the objective was to kill perhaps, but that was secondary. The most important thing for those men was to die the flaming death, to commit the suicide of social despair. Ripon Hall was nothing like that; the confusing element was the facelessness of Ripon Hall. The students in there were not particular individuals—they were black men, nameless black men who might be students, who might be anybody. This is, of course, a tactic, using black anonymity to frighten the white, the whitey, the honky in all of us, liberals, conservatives, bigots, even whites with serious overidentification problems with blacks. See, there is this blank building, Ripon Hall, and these nameless, uncategorized blacks in it, and that is precisely the shape that black nihilism presents to whites. The consequence is a terrible scene in our imaginations, the Sack of Constantinople. The chairman has his throat cut, the white secretary undergoes ritual rape, the building is fired as the police make ready to storm it, and these incomprehensible figures do a death-of-the-gods before our horrified eyes.

"It didn't fit the data, though. Neither in Wagner nor in life is the great nihilistic assertion of despairing self-destruction preceded by calling a press conference. In another culture it's possible, but then the act of self-immolation has other meanings, as when the Buddhists incinerated themselves to protest the continuation of the Vietnam War. Here there have been a few cases of such *auto-da-fé*, self-inflicted, but then it was by white liberals, absolutely insane people who conceived an act that was too foreign to have meaning. The lady who goes to a parking lot or a shopping center, pours kerosene, and lights the match lacks grandeur; she's not heroic, she's crazy, and what she's done is too sickening to be morally instructive.

"And the list of demands. One kills one's self because it's harmonic with a tragic life situation, or as an act of defiance against injustice which has become insupportable, more than the animating spirit can sustain, but a *Götterdämmerung* for a five-point program, neatly typed out and Xeroxed? Impossible. The more I thought about it as I was waiting for the telephone call, the more certain I was the call would be made, had to be made. The people in the building were after meat and potatoes. They weren't ideologues. They had no metaphysic that would urge them to destroy themselves. They wanted to bargain and they were looking for power levers, not war. They would see that by holding the chairman they would be forcing the Administration's hand. They would understand that they were making the Administration resort to superior force, which obviates any bargaining, so they wouldn't do it, so they would let the professor go, and when they did that the haggling could start. It became apparent to me that McVey's fears were groundless. We weren't dealing with the undealable, something intrinsically outside his experience or our institutional framework. We had only to wait and be prepared to give a little when the chairman was freed. So I called McVey and told him that. He was noncommittal, but it turned out I was absolutely right."

Apparently, B.J. was most responsible for letting the chairman and his secretary go. The city councilman had come and been allowed into the building's vestibule; he had been permitted to enter with misgivings and reluctance. As at the press conference, only Tully and B.J. appeared, and only Tully spoke to him. The councilman said, "Let the chairman go, they'll let you keep the building; if you don't let the chairman go, it's your ass." It was a short conversation. The councilman had come as a favor to the Mayor. He didn't want to get close to any of this for fear it would be *his* ass, so he said his piece, three or four times in slightly different ways, answered a couple of questions, and got out. He never phoned McVey, would say nothing to the watching newsmen outside, and waited till the next day to tell the Mayor.

Tully and B.J. went upstairs where all fifty or so who were in the building were meeting. Tully passed on what the councilman had said, and they began to debate. Except B.J. He said nothing. He always said nothing. It was part of his power with them. He talked so seldom that when he did they listened.

B.J. sat on the floor, his back against the wall, his legs drawn up and his head almost between them. From time to time he'd bring his head up and wipe his glasses or take out his pipe, doodle with it, and put his head back. It was the position he'd used to live through the eighteen-hour meetings Snick used to have in the South. There he had talked more because he had believed more and hoped more. Now he believed not at all. When people asked him what he was studying, he'd say, "VIC—that stands for Very Inorganic Chemistry."

He didn't want to be in Ripon Hall. He wanted to study chemistry and live with his chick, who was a registered nurse, who supported him, who was white, who was a good enough chick so that for the first time he'd asked himself what *she* got out of it. It was good enough between the two of them that he asked her. She said she had him. He asked if that was enough for working, for paying the rent, for taking the clothes to the automat, for buying the food, for everything. She said it was. He asked how. She said because B.J. was sweet and loved her. He said he'd never told her he loved her, and she'd said she knew that, but some time he would because he did. It did come to him after a while that he did, and as he half listened to the discussion repeat itself, he was sorry he hadn't told her.

He had a bad feeling about this action. He'd had no part in planning it, didn't believe in it. They'd come to him as his father's friends had come to collect his father for the NAACP meetings, and his father had always gone, not because he believed any good would come of it, but because, as he used to tell B.J., "If you're a good race man, you come with 'em when they as' you to." His father had told him once that, when he was a young man, he had believed, but his enthusiasm had been worn down and he didn't believe any more.

B.J. certainly didn't believe in this. He didn't see where Eldon Russell, Jr., was any worse a white man than two hundred others on the campus. Some of the other stuff was all right, but this black history, black psychology, black everything was crap. B.J. was mournfully convinced that no amount of chanting "black is beautiful" would make the black man believe it. "It's the same with others like it is me an' you. We watch the television an' leap up an' say, 'Hey, they got a nigger in that commercial, well, my, my, my!' "

Black was not beautiful to B.J. It wasn't ugly, but it wasn't beautiful. White was beautiful to B.J. That was what first attracted him to his chick. He liked white girls better. *That* was a subject he'd never discussed with his father. He wanted to, but his father wasn't receptive to any talk about sex. Never thought it was seemly, and to talk about sex with a white woman might have seemed to mean something he didn't mean.

Where B.J. grew up they talked about getting white pussy. He wanted some very much, and he was not like Eldridge Cleaver: "I, a black man, confronted The Ogre—the white woman. . . . Was it true, did I really prefer white girls over black? The conclusion was clear and inescapable: I did. . . . As a matter of principle, it was of paramount importance to me to have an antagonistic, ruthless attitude toward white women. . . . I became a rapist." Which is good if you can do it. B.J. was raped and castrated by a white girl named Charlotte in a shacky house outside of Pickens, Mississippi, and it made him permanently pessimistic about black being beautiful or allowing himself to be too conscious of there being races. Very Inorganic Chemistry.

Charlotte and her white girl friend should not have been with the voter registration team. There was a general agreement that races and sexes should not be mixed in the rural areas, because it increased the opposition of the whites and the reluctance of the blacks to go down to the courthouse and "redish" to vote. Project directors in other places in the state would not have whites of either sex, so sometimes there were more white volunteers than there were willing voter registration projects. That was why B.J. took the white boy to work with him, the two other blacks, and the black girl. One of the blacks was a jive ass who hustled Charlotte and the other girl into the project in some complicated, double-talking way.

For a few days it worked, but the jive ass and his friend started telling Charlotte and the other girl to prove, really prove, really, really, really prove they believed in equality by offering up some white pussy. The four of them got to drinking wine, smoking grass, and staying up late, flirting and baiting each other and getting each other excited and sleeping late and not going out to see the people to get them to "redish." They had a climactic night of pseudo rape, slapping, punishment, copulation, and ecstasy, while the white boy and B.J. in one room and the black girl alone in the other tried to sleep.

B.J. talked a lot at them. It didn't work. He beat up one of the black boys. It didn't work. He drove to Jackson, to the state headquarters, and demanded they get the two white girls out. They told him he was the project director and he should do it. He tried to explain how hard it was. Well, they said, they would send someone down to look into it. But they didn't, so B.J. drove back and Charlotte got him alone, touching him all over and asking snidely, "Won't or can't? Won't or can't?" Finally a white woman and B.J. couldn't. It was demoralizing, and beating up the jive ass and the other black kid didn't re-establish B.J.'s primacy.

He despised them; work fell off and the project disintegrated. The black girl left in a humiliated rage. Jive ass and his pal ran off the white boy and then finally left themselves. Now it was the three of them and B.J. was scared—two white women and a black man alone in the shacky house. He began smoking grass and gave up trying to redish people. Charlotte went on playing with him till she succeeded and then, instead of making love, she began yelling to her girl friend, "Look, come see, B.J.'s hard. He's got it up." It would have been more humiliating if B.J. hadn't been so demoralized by then.

The girls wouldn't work. Charlotte said she was working, fixing up a library for the black schoolchildren out of a few boxes of books donated by liberal white ladies up North. It should have taken a day. Charlotte hadn't finished in three weeks. The other girl spent her time writing lies to her friends up north about the Ku Klux Klan being after her. At last they went away. The white woman is an ogre.

In Ripon Hall they were still discussing what to do about the chairman and his secretary when B.J. lifted his head after an especially long period of keeping it between his legs. "Let 'em go," B.J. said, and they agreed that would be the best thing to do.

Excerpts from the Verbal History Project:

MIRSKY: When the black student called I attempted to set up some regular channel of communication, which I now felt was possible. The answer to my suggestion was maybe, maybe, but not until after Afro Day tomorrow. . . . I arrived at Fletcher Hall about the time word had come that the chairman and his secretary had been released without harm. The same people were in McVey's office as earlier in the evening, with the addition of President Hungerford. I could see that what I'd been told about Hungerford was true. He'd flown back to the city and was taking a hard line about Afro Day. His position was that no accommodation to the black demands was possible, that Afro Day was a violation of Regulation XXVII, and he made a big point of saying that it had been the first violation of the Regulation that had led to the blacks' action. Then they had a discussion among them, during which I first became aware that they had taken action to punish the students involved in the police car and Rennecker Hall. I couldn't believe it. I told them they were opening a two-front war. The timing was incredible. McVey looked miserable, poor man. I deduced he had been overruled. He said nothing. Always, from start to finish, McVey was loyal to Hungerford. He never said a word against the man.

I was disturbed, but it seemed the letters summoning the Rennecker Hall culprits had gone out and would be delivered in the morning, so I said a prayer and stayed silent. Besides, I was more worried about Afro Day, which Hungerford was going on about like Henry Clay Frick talking about breaking up a steel workers' strike. I tried to tell the man that the black thing was not the same; this wasn't SDS—I don't care what anybody said then or says now. Their action was radical in method but conventional in objective. These weren't revolutionaries but people who wanted to be cut in on the pie. I remember I kept saying—I'm excitable, I think I must have shouted, "It's a dealable situation, so deal!" Something like that I said. Hungerford, you know the way he does, he humphs himself up so he looks like a bladder with a bow tie and a business suit, and tells me *I'm* naive. This man who has spent the last generation with millionaires and has no better idea of what is happening on the streets of America than the, the, well, Joint Chiefs of Staff. He said some more stuff, and I got mad. I told him, "You want to be Clark Kerr or Grayson Kirk, you go ahead. It'll cost you your job, but the faculty isn't going to let you cooperate with the radicals in putting this University up against the wall!"

MC TAVISH: Mirsky lost control of himself. He was shaking a finger at Hungerford and shouting, "You and Roger Elias ought to be in a conspiracy to polarize this institution, so you can have what you both want, the last great confrontation." Hungerford was very crisp in his reply, "You're naive," he said. "If we accept these demands we would be turning over the facilities and resources of this institution for a training school for black revolutionaries. I will not negotiate with students under any circumstances. I will listen to them, but there will not be any changes made at this University along the lines of the black demands." In my opinion, Mirsky had lost control of himself, but he said one thing to Hungerford that shook him. He was talking a lot of what I would call sentimental, liberal trash, but then he said, "Dr. Hungerford, tonight you can forget there are four hundred thousand blacks all around this campus—" oh, yes, he interrupted himself to make a gratuitous slam—"I don't see how you can forget it when you've spent years evicting them and building a *cordon sanitaire* around this institution, but if you have, and you do something foolish tomorrow, then they, not me, *they* will remind you."

I knew as soon as he said it, from the expression on President Hungerford's face, we were going to be wishy-washy. He didn't say anything to Mirsky. In fact, our discussion stopped until Mirsky was eased out. When he was gone, McVey immediately said the Mayor's office was concerned about a reaction in the ghetto.

HUNGERFORD: I had been out of town when this crisis developed. I flew back as quickly as I could, but I arrived late and was not sufficiently informed to do more than accept the advice of my colleagues.

MC VEY: We met until very late. It was a lively meeting. Professor Mirsky joined us for awhile, if memory serves. It was generally felt that it would be better to hold off making any hard and fast decisions, as we'd asked several distinguished black urbanologists from Harvard-MIT to fly out and make contact with Ripon Hall.

VII

IN THE FIRST full light of the next day, the assistant curator of the DuPont Museum was moving around with a ladder and a Hasselblad camera. The rest of the campus was dormant. Only a few white sympathizers had stayed the night in front of Ripon. They talked in slow drowsiness to themselves and to several faculty members who had volunteered to stay to keep the peace. A slight ground fog gave the lawns and gardens a blue wash and threw a light on the ornamented buildings that was more softly European than American.

It was still excellent light for photography, for the sun was yet too low in the sky to create a shadow problem for the curator, who was taking pictures of Sil's new effort, "The Black Souls of White Folks." This exhibition was mostly hung from the branches of trees. One piece, called "Integration," was a huge ball of mouths, anuses, and genitalia, both male and female, attacking, biting, ramming, sticking, enclosing, clamping, and snapping at each other in a sphere of perpetual misery. Another, "And God Created White Man," was a large aerosol can which was spraying out horrible-headed infants whose flesh had the surprising, sunless whiteness of the fungi that grow on the underside of rotting logs. "Emancipation Proclamation" was so lifelike that people turning the corner of the chemistry building and seeing it dangling from a tree were exclaiming in sick shock all day: it was the swinging body of a lynched and castrated Negro. The curator was defeated in his efforts to make a satisfactory picture of "Communication." For this Sil had taken an entire tree and scattered over it what looked like flowers, until you got close. Then you could see that every blossom was a knotted cluster of tongues, some of which were rigid and some made to move with the wind. All of them conveyed the impression of the distended cry of suffering, and some of them were fixed with devices which made them hiss and shriek when a breeze blew. "Christmas Tree" was wholly decorated in brightly colored, stylized instruments of torture and death—thumbscrews, blackjacks, spears, revolvers, whips, branding irons, barbed arrows, mace. The curator stole one of the ornaments before he took pictures of the "White Washing Machine Contraption," a tall, straight-up thing that would bulge and shrink, ripple and rigidify. It looked somewhat like a gastrointestinal tract; from its base there came in much amplified waves the sounds of swallowing, digesting, belching, hiccuping, farting, and defecating.

Ellie Rector woke up that morning with her mind on freedom or peace or some expansive, liberating thought. This soaring spirit inside her gained altitude when the mail came with a letter summoning her again to Rennecker Hall for disciplinary action. This time she didn't look upon it with deadened uncertainty, but as an avoidable unpleasantness which she could put up with or not.

Shapiro called as before, but this time he asked her to cross the campus and go to the rooming house where Roger Elias lived to bring him to a meeting. Roger had no phone, and it was imperative that he know about the "daily atrocity," which, it appeared, had landed in the mailboxes of more than the original Norman Thomas Five. Quickly she said she'd go out of curiosity to see how Roger lived. She wanted very much to make sense out of Roger and the others, these people who never suffered from her nebulous melancholies, her impression of having been robbed of something but not knowing what, her feeling that her life was an endless postponed waiting, a permanently deferred climax that would not happen and that she could not resign herself to not happening.

Making her way through Manion Gate, thinking about these things brought her up against the White Washing Machine Contraption. She gasped. Painting and sculpture were distant attractions for her. In New York, Paris, and Rome she had stood next to her father, regarding the most famous pieces of art, aware that they could hold her interest for less than a minute. Sil's work was different. She spent five minutes looking at the White Washing Machine Contraption, maybe because Sil's things moved and made noises, or because they were funny or disgusting or horrible. He was horrible. She was surprised that she could be as interested in someone she truly felt was revolting. Her roommate had taken one look at Sil and said, "Yech! *I* don't even want to meet him." And what kind of a relationship . . . how could he and Slob Child . . . what did they . . . ? The half-finished questions rushed on top of each other in anger at a girl her age, possibly from a family not too different from Ellie's, being treated like that, allowing herself to be treated like that, and by Sil, who was about Ellie's age, maybe a few years older, but still someone who could have been like the boys she'd always known.

She stared at the White Washing Machine Contraption and drew a meaning from it. When Sil saw people like herself, they looked like that to him. Like that pillar with the sick, mouth-like organ on top of it, chopping its teeth or whatever together, snapping and turning like a heliotrope casting around for its sun, that endlessly trapping, eating, masticating mouth on top of a column of slurping and smacking physiological parts, the sum point of which was defecation. The contraption made an offensive, cloacal noise which made Ellie want to back off from it, but she stood her ground, keeping her eyes on it, thinking on Sil and Slob Child. Who was the Slob Child or Monique? Was she always like that or had Sil made her that way, the way men do, by suggesting to her that was the kind of woman he wanted, an inversion of the woman killing herself with diets, exercise, and beauty treatments to be her husband's dream girl?

Ellie discovered she couldn't defy Sil's statue. She left it, walking a bit more quickly, till she came on "And God Created White Man," taking shape out of the areosol can that Sil had designed with a label that reminded her of all labels on all cans. There were letters on the label which made up into words, or didn't: STUFF . . . ECH . . . GUNK . . . FLUFF . . . SOUPER . . . SOUPERIOR . . . SOUPERIORITY . . . YESTIMATE . . . TESTIMA . . . TESTIMATO SOUPER . . . FLUFFOUS . . . FIRST SLOE GIZZ . . . ERFIC . . . FLUFF . . . STUFF.

Her mind began reviewing television ads. Now-generation people, her age, her face, her race at barbecues, in convertibles with surfboards in the back seat, smoking cigarettes walking in the woods, sticking hands down to reach ice cubes for Cokes, Canada Drys, and 7-Ups, gargling and getting kissed, brushing teeth and getting kissed, spraying under arms and getting kissed, frolicking youth getting kissed, marvelous people photographed in their completed development. It was true, Ellie decided, if you use those products and do those things you do get kissed and you do run around being happy. But you know, at the same time there's the question, Is this all, there's nothing else, it goes on like this till wrinkles?

Plastic. That was the word people used to put things down. Plastic parents, plastic home, plastic aerosol cans out of which come plastic—plastic school, plastic people, plastic Ellie. A boy with a lot of leftish art talk had actually called her plastic once; it had sounded like a dare to go to bed with him, like shaming a girl for her virginity, so she'd shrugged it off. Now Sil had the plastic people coming out of their can and it was striking and made you think, but plastic wasn't all that bad. The real daily atrocity was getting up and asking, Well, is that all? When you begin to stop waiting for life to begin, when stone and bone, souper fluffous and testimato, God—you agree it must be maternity, skiing, or sports-car racing with a man who'll say, yes, that's all.

Sil, Shapiro, the Supreme Cream, Roger—if they were saying, stone and bone, first sloe gizz, white washing, bowel moving machine contraption, lynched black man strung out on a tongue-tied tree, if they were saying that, if they were saying, eech, fluff, that is not all, you are of the now-generation, my girl, and now is the time, and you will feel things and know things you did not know before, and you will become excited and tired, cry and be hilarious, and you will join with people, and together with them you will say no, this is not all, then, bone and stone, Ellie is a radical, too.

Roger lived in the ghetto. The rooming house was about two blocks past the outermost perimeter patrolled by the University's private police. It made Ellie nervous, but no one bothered her. She made it up dirty stairs to a door that had been broken into and repaired so many times there was no place on it for another lock. Roger hollered at her to come in. She found a neat, almost empty place; one chair, one table, one cot, an inflatable mattress with Roger on it, a few clothes hung on a bar, a few shirts in a suitcase, some books and papers, nicely stacked. Ellie had expected bedlam; Roger *was* sort of a human eggbeater.

He pushed the blanket away and was out of bed, walking around and talking, wearing boxer shorts which made his legs look emaciated. There was nothing to him. Tall with a concave chest. Stewing meat, Ellie thought, and it would be a grey stew. Roger was orating, ignorant that his flesh had been graded suitable for tallow and ragout. He dressed, lecturing her on how the establishment was unable to listen to its own best tacticians and did the work of radicalizing that he couldn't do without them.

"Marx was wrong on the details, but not on the essence. The system's contradictions do destroy it, destroy it. . . . A few puny people, and they've got to crush us, but they've got too much power, and that's why we can play jiujitsu on them, exploit the inconsistencies of the power to turn it back on them . . . Goddamn . . . the daily atrocity . . . and the timing, if they'd asked me I couldn't have picked a better time. It's still impossible, I don't believe it. I told Shapiro last night when he was saying they wouldn't do anything till the semester is over. I told him that's what *you'd* do or *I'd* do, the smarter thing for them with the blacks rising; and what's the dumbest, the most stupid possible act you can conceive of? It's· repudiate the agreement and go after the people of the police car, but I never thought they would do it so fast. I figured they'd wait a few weeks at least. The motherfuckers are putting themselves up against the wall, so now we will have the revolution."

Ellie was lifted up by his intensity as he moved her down the stairs and the streets toward the campus. She absorbed his energy, not remembering her yen to pry a little into his life, and when she did remember she wondered if he had any other life.

"The real question now," Roger was yammering at her, "is can there be socialism on one campus only? Can there? Can there? Answer that."

"I don't know (what you're talking about)," Ellie said. She nearly had to run to keep up with him.

"There will be a revolution at the University. We'll get control. The Administration will force the liberals, one by one and all at once, to make a choice, and they'll choose us and then we'll make a revolution. What's going to happen after that? We, here, in control, in power, the University liberated, turned around, prevented from fulfilling its assigned functions as the trainer of personnel, the technical complex for industry and the government. Outside they'll mass against us to recapture their campus from its students and teachers, but maybe they'll leave us alone, or . . . or . . . what an *or* that will be! The reoccupation of the campus by the Right. . . . Reoccupation of what's left of it. . . . There'll be serious destruction . . . it won't be as easy for them as in other places. . . . We won't have a Sproul Hall here, eight hundred people allowing themselves to be toted off like nonviolent potato sacks."

Ellie was too intimidated to ask Roger to walk slower, but she had to ask him what would happen here if it was to be different from Berkeley.

"I told you. There'll be lots of destruction. I mean, I can see some people getting hurt, really getting hurt."

"But the students are going to lose?"

"No. I didn't say that. A revolution isn't a big battle that's settled all in one day. A revolution does have its evolution. First Berkeley, then Columbia, now us, each different, each more developed politically and tactically, each politicizing more people on every campus. You had the attack on the Moncada Army Camp which was beaten; after that Fidel came in the Granma and landed and went up into the Sierra Maestra. 1905 came before 1917. There must be developmental defeat to win."

Ellie would have had trouble understanding what he was talking about if the two of them had been quietly sitting.

Trotting two steps behind him, out of breath and missing a key word here and there, made it incomprehensible, except she gathered that Roger was a revolutionary and not for kidding. That was exciting.

Roger's sense of the moment in front of a crowd was unmatched by a similar gift for understanding individuals. Either he didn't care, or he didn't know that Ellie could scarcely make sense out of what he was saying. She was quiet, not offering opposition, and for an audience of one that was all Roger asked. He got to a point in his oratory that was so important to him he stopped, faced her, and declared: "Che said, 'We needn't always wait for the revolutionary conditions to be present; the insurrection itself can create them.' And that's what's happening in America and here at the University. The insurrections on all the campuses have created a New Class and given it consciousness. It's not a peace movement, a student power movement, a black movement. It's the self-discovery of the New Class of the powerless, of youth, of intellectuals, of professionals, of technicians and students, the necessary people of this society who make and tend the machines, human, mechanical, and electronic, which they have no control over in an artificially created, morally neutral, freezing cold universe."

When they got to the campus Ellie lost him in the crowd of waiting people that had grown anew in front of Ripon Hall where Shapiro was supposed to be looking for them. The mood was disputive but not combative the way it had been the day before, perhaps because the antis weren't yet out in critical numbers, or perhaps the possibility of an unknown quantity of blacks arriving had made them cautious. The crowd was split into groups of five to twenty-five, arguing over what was going on. Some of the most prestigious senior faculty were there and taking part, the sort who by legend are indifferent to students, concerned only with their research and their relations with the government. Like Anatol Wiegel, the Nobel Prize winner in chemistry.

"My dear young man," he was saying, "I came to this country to escape the brutalities of a well-organized minority group that was also as sincerely convinced it was right as you are. And it was right about some things; you are right about some things, but you can't destroy everything to be right about something."

"Sir," the student he was arguing with said, "didn't you help build the atom bomb?"

"Yes, I helped. We didn't know but the Nazis might get it first. We knew they were working on it. We didn't know they were on the wrong track. We couldn't take the risk. I helped Fermi and the others, just a little because it's not my field. But if it had been, young man, I would have done more."

"Sir," the young man pressed, not in the style of a debater about to make a clever point but with the passion of conviction, "wasn't that destroying everything to be right about something? Wasn't it, sir? Wasn't it much more than what we're doing here?"

"I can't agree with you at all. First, this is a university, not a sovereign state with its own army—"

"Sir, I don't mean to interrupt you," the student said.

"You should let me finish, but go ahead if it's something you feel you have to say right now."

"It is, Professor Wiegel. It's that the University is the extension of the state. It's part of the state, it does the state's work, it built the bomb. We believe that the myth of the University being a private institution, not connected with the state, has prevented people from looking at it realistically and critically. The universities mobilize for war, they design the weapons systems, and when they're challenged they say they're not the state, they don't decide peace and war, they don't determine our imperialist foreign policy . . . oh, no, they only make it possible by supplying the armaments."

"No, no, no," the chemist responded. "This is not a satisfactory definition. This is a useless way of looking at things, young man. If I accept how you come to define the University as part of the state, then it follows we are all, as you say, 'extensions of the state.' Even obeying the red traffic signal becomes an act supportive of the state and in some remote sense of our so-called imperialist foreign policy. What you, I think mistakenly, consider an extension of the state is the necessary interconnection between individual people and institutions in any society, be they very simple ones or highly complex ones. Because I go to work in the morning that does not mean I give my assent to what the American minister in Ouagadougou could be doing."

The student was shaking his head all the time Professor Wiegel was talking. "And what you're saying, sir," he said as soon as he politely could, "is that we can be good Americans and use the same cop-out the Germans used about supporting the Nazis. Isn't that what they said? 'We only lived in the society, we were just people caught in it going to work in the morning, and you shouldn't take that to mean we supported the government or knew what it was doing.' Isn't that the same thing?"

The chemist was quiet for a minute, thinking about the proposition, and this gave the student a chance to add, "Isn't that why you left Germany, sir? You aren't Jewish, are you? You didn't have to leave? Why did you leave? Didn't you leave because just being there, just being what you called part of the necessary interconnections of society made you an accomplice, and you didn't want to be an accomplice to the Nazis?"

"Yes, in a way that's true. I did not want to be part of them at all. I did not even want to breathe the same air they did, or eat the same food or see the same mountains, which I loved but which were ruined for me by the thought they were enjoying them, too. That is true. Every man should have some line, some final line inside him, and when that is reached he tears up his contract with that society."

"That's what we're doing here, Professor Wiegel."

"Yes, but it's ridiculous. At this University? In this country? My God, you can't compare the two. You don't know what the Nazis were like. I hear you young men talking about fascism. You think fascism is the old war movies they show on the television. It isn't. I can't tell you how terrible the real thing was. A young person like you would be dead or in the camps. It is not the same. This is America, and you must have a sense of proportion."

As they spoke they were encircled by listening people, one of whom boomed out, "We have a sense of proportion. We are the first generation that refuses to be Good Americans. We're the first to recognize our own concentration camps, which we call ghettos. Mr. Wiegel, there is an American concentration camp right outside the gates of this campus, and we're going to tear it down. Will you join us?"

"Of course I will join," the old scholar and anti-Nazi said. "Why do you think I come to talk to you. I will join you in tearing down the ghettos, but not in tearing down the University, not the University. Not all the work of the hand of man is evil."

All of them were silent for a bit. The young ones looked at the old one, who stood his ground without embarrassment or temper. The first student now came back at him softly.

"Sir," he said, "why did you help them build the bomb? Didn't you ever think that you were helping imperialists conquer fascists? Wouldn't it have been better to let them destroy each other by carrying on a war that ultimately would have created revolutions against all the governments involved? This way you beat the Nazis, you invented the bomb, and you perpetuated the whole system of international war."

Wiegel sighed. "Young man, your analysis depends on a pragmatic judgment which I think is completely erroneous, and behind it is a bad doctrine. You teach that in accordance with a hypothetical reading of the laws of history, we should sacrifice the living generation for a future one. I think that is a very bad teaching."

"So instead," the student answered, and forgot to say sir, "you invented the bomb and sacrificed the future for the present, your generation for ours. Why should we listen to you, Dr. Wiegel?"

Excerpt from the Verbal History Project:

YALDELL: Even on the morning of Afro Day things weren't out of control. It was getting messy, but it wasn't a disaster. Most of the University was running normally. I should say all of it, because the classes that met in Ripon Hall had pretty much found other places. The blacks were invisible inside of Frederick Douglass University. The only trouble they were causing was the rumors: Malcolm X was going to rise from his grave, Stokely was about to make an appearance, or Rap Brown, Huey Newton, Dick Gregory, all the folk heroes, and of course, Mungo, our local Mau-Mau. He was expected with ten thousand followers. These rumors stoked the fire. Even though we have a campus with thirty thousand liberal whites—or just about—and all of them consider themselves brothers under the skin to the black man, people weren't sure some invading black army would know it.

What we needed was leadership. People were coming up to me all morning, you know, asking what was going to happen, what the Administration was going to do. I called Blackie McTavish several times and asked him, and he told me damned if he knew. He said he had gotten Pomfret to suggest to Fletcher Hall some kind of announcement be made. It didn't have to say much, just something saying the campus would be open to all normal student activities, oh God, yes, including speechmaking and rallies, but was closed to any outside activity coming here. I don't think it would have taken any more than that.

INTERVIEWER: What did Fletcher Hall think of the suggestion?

YALDELL: You'll have to ask Blackie that. When I talked to him he was still waiting for a ring back. In my opinion— oh, I shouldn't say that, but I had the feeling that Hungerford would have bought it. The story was that McVey and later on Pomfret argued against it on the grounds they'd worked so hard to get what black students we had and that we should be very careful. There was another story that it was the police who wanted to go easy, lie back and wait. I'd heard the Mayor is supposed to have said, "I don't want the first battle of the summer race war opened by our force on the University campus." That's third or fourth hand, one of the stories that was going around.

For whatever reasons, they laid back, waited, and it was a disaster. I'd like to put in here how very unfair I think the Administration's lack of leadership was to the majority of students who come here to learn and love this school, more or less as it is, not as Mr. Roger Elias wants to change it into a basic training camp for Fidelistas, Maoists, and other assorted anarchist nuts. I don't want to go on and on this way, but I still can't believe what went on here in one of the top ten schools in the world. I work closely with the undergraduates; that's why my office is here in the Union. I can't tell you the educational damage this did. Oh, I know everybody is talking about our passionate, modern, with-it, now, engaged, dedicated, alienated, radical youth. Well, let me tell you that set of adjectives fits about one kid in thirty or less—or it did before all of this started. They probably are all radicals now. We've taught them that, a few teen-age Trotskys, mini-Maos, and baby Bolsheviki—say, how do you like that alliteration? I must be another Roger Elias. Anyway, these romper-room radicals probably have taught the majority of our students to accept the communist coming as inevitable and gotten them to join it. When a place like this can't produce the leadership to resist being run over and taken over, I'm accusing more than Fletcher Hall or weakness in the Administration. I'm accusing the faculty, too. Some of them were openly and flagrantly on Elias' side; others I could name—and will if I get mad enough—were double-agents or dupes or I don't know. Maybe they were well intentioned, but you know what the road to hell is paved with, and I thought that was just something grandmother used to say until I lived through this. I admit this is the first time in my life I'd ever been in a real political situation, something besides tame stuff like elections. Boy, isn't that a laugh to say something like that in this country and mean it?

Afro Day began somewhat after noon with the slow and not very militant arrival of a modest number of blacks from off campus. They put up signs, arranged for sound equipment and other paraphernalia needed to play music, exhibit paintings and statues, perform the dance, and hold meetings. There was nothing menacing about the operation. Just the reverse. It enticed the white students forward to see what the long-robed man sitting under the sign "Black History" might have to say. There were other signs and discussion leaders for Third World, Black Personality, Islam, Civil Rights Movement or Human Rights Revolution?, The Black Soldier, Can a Black Man Be a Christian?, Future of the Races, Black Separatism, Black Family in White America. On a stage several musical groups began performing to illustrate a lecture on The Varieties of Black Music in Old World and New. This drew a large audience who clapped hands and tapped feet to music from West Africa to Brazil and the Caribbean.

The Square had been changed into a fair or an educational entertainment. Students and faculty came forward and took part in large numbers. A door in Frederick Douglass University was opened, and some of its people came out to join in. The visiting off-campus blacks moved in and out of the building freely; whites were turned away, but politely, by a young man who smiled and said, "This is our thing in here. We have a thing for you out there," pointing to the Square. Mungo and fifty of his Big Black Cats marched through Manion Gate chanting cadences in what the whites took to be Swahili. Their close order drill was very good, better even than the marching bands from those Southern, all-Negro state colleges where the students are trained exclusively in football and pageantry. When the Big Black Cats weren't marching, they were standing in stiff lines, eyes straight ahead, like ghetto incarnations of the Buckingham Palace Guards, peacefully proud.

Black pride / white appreciation. The ghetto of blackly beautiful men and women. A ghetto to be, projected, planned, hoped for, ghetto abolished, ghetto re-established. The people on the Square gave themselves over to these hopes, the blacks letting down their guard, letting themselves be taken in by white brother's happy assent, the whites forgetting old crimes and present realities, forgetting the regular and constant retributions. For several hours the people were taken up by possibilities of union or splitting off in peace and mutual appreciation. Remission from social pain. That good spirit held as the sun began to go down and the blacks put up their signs and their musical instruments and their hand-worked jewelry, statues, and clothes, and it worked as five Fuckheads, clad in orange-and-white-striped tunics, brass rings, and mocking black and green masks, did a leaping dance on the lawn. Sil's Ashanti tribesmen.

Out from under the good spirit, still holding, there crumbled the ghetto's detritus. They had silted and sifted onto the campus, unrecognizable among the other blacks, these ones, bored, broke, disconnected, the truly irrelevant, dangerous black, male adolescent, do-bopper, prowler, vandal, disadvantaged, two-legged urban problem; needing case work, father figures, vocational guidance, apprentice training; in flight from cop, truant officer, parole board, and psychiatrist; urban problem child, child of the urban problem, demoralized, unmotivated hustler, alienated, hostile boy of destructive gang loyalty, unaspiring pimp, victim/ victimizer; putting quarters in the box, throwing bricks through the window, looter, tosser of the epithet and the cocktail, dreamer of no other man's dream, arsonist, committer of crime on the street, begetter of promiscuous children, psychopath, sociopath creeping through indescribable mind-sets, dragging your dependent, demoralized, acquisitive gestalt onto the campus; you, you maker of nightmares come true, you functional illiterate, you welfare sponge, unproductive grouting turning to sand between the bricks of tenement walls, you had to come and rape the girl in the Mitchell Library washroom, come to run through the Square exercising your right to practice your unique, intimidating, nonchalant terror.

There weren't many of them running in the green shadows of dusk, a hundred at most in the midst of several thousand students and faculty who backed off and away from them, cast up from the ghetto, brought onto the campus by who knows what formulations of militancy, adventure, piracy, and hate. No slogans were shouted, only a few "whities" and a couple of "motherfuckers"; they appeared to have no special objective and no strong leader, for they broke up into two groups, one grabbing a white student and beating him while the other part of the band ran toward first one building and then another.

The whites, who outnumbered the black teen-agers by twenty to one, backed off, telling each other in whispered shouts, "Don't make it worse. Let's not start anything. Just stay away from them." So they would back off, and then, when the black kids would change direction, they would come forward, always staying a safe distance. Even the jocks were immobilized. A large bunch of them stood on the steps directly in front of the Minerva, obeying the adjurations of the swimming coach to stay cool. They did so without straining, telling each other what a helluva deal it was, but nobody made the speech that says, well-what-are-we-waiting-for-are-we-going-to-let-those-fuckers-tear-down-our-college-brick-by-brick?

No one rescued the student who was being beaten. They watched, expressing the sentiments you'd expect, but instead of acting, the people making up this amorphous crowd asked each other why somebody didn't do something. The black kids didn't beat the student badly. They appeared to lose interest in him because they found they could run directly at a segment of the onlooking whites, who would run away, panting and out of condition. This they did for ten minutes in a sequence of runs made strange by the silence. No cries, no shouts, merely the panted breathing of the white herd being chased about the Square.

Ellie, aglistening and alight, went to and fro with the white herd, but so slowly the black teen-agers might have gotten her—assuming they wanted to. The Supreme Cream got her instead, and, taking her by an arm, he reassembled as best he could words Shapiro had told him: "These blacks aren't politically developed. They're very angry; they have no way of telling their friends from their enemies. They're an unfocused, insurrectionary force, revolutionary in emotion but not in consciousness, so you have to stay away from them."

"Cream, I want to watch."

"You'll get hurt."

"I don't care if I get hurt—well, I do. Can I stay with you? Will that slow you down? Would you take me with you? I want to watch."

So they stayed in the back of the crowd and watched the underprivileged rampage. They saw B.J. and Tully Haskins come running with some others from the direction of Ripon; saw B.J. go up to one of the culturally deprived, look him in the face, drop his forearms over the ghetto boy's shoulders, and cheek almost touching cheek, walk him backwards talking into his ear; saw Tully running as fast as he could toward the University bookstore, crying out, waving, signaling, shouting, "No, man! No! No! Don't do it!" Saw Tully was too late, and the noise of plate glass breaking, the whoosh of smoke, disconcerting black in contrast to the orange of its flame and the grays, lavenders, and blues of the dusk; gave ground with the whites and heard the dismayed nooos! articulated on long, aghast, sucked-in breaths. "That's the bookstore! They've set fire to the bookstore!"

The Supreme Cream left Ellie to help whites and University blacks put out the fire, while the rampaging deprived moved their storm into the Owl Cove, upsetting the tables, throwing a chair at the juke box and attempting to overturn the steam table. But B.J. and Tully got to them, calmed them, put more arms around shoulders, guided them out of the building—the white herd giving ground as B.J. and Tully gathered them together and walked them out

Manion Gate, saying to the blighted children of urban rot, "Stay cool, brothers."

The two started back to Ripon Hall with Tully half doing the sideways skip of a basketball player so he would be facing B.J. But B.J. wasn't listening to his talk. Tully had just told him about the incident in Mitchell Library, and with that B.J. tuned him out. Bless the mothers that get it up, bless them for what they do to our own women, bless them for what they do to whitey's women, bless them; bless them now for they have never lived the good, golden hour of Bob Moses in Mississippi, talking of going out among the people and touching them, bless them for they have not seen fear die, have not made the small touch of hand lightly on hand by which hope is conferred back to the old by the young; bless these motherfuckers for coming here and ruining an hour of hope for us and for themselves, bless them for the remembrance of the conversations outside the courthouse when the Mississippi people redished, bless the Mississippi people for wanting to build something of their own, bless the no-good jive cats for the reminder you've got to get it up and keep it up against whitey, bless whitey for letting us burn down his damn University, bless, bless, bless all us excuses for people.

Sil's five Ashanti tribesmen danced by, preceded by Slob Child wearing a Marilyn Monroe mask, shouldering a power pack, and aiming a bright light at the warriors who were doing long leaps in unison. Sil, with motion picture camera, was photographing.

"I'd like to kick their ass good," said B.J.

We tried negotiation and a token picket line,
But Mr. Charlie didn't see us—he might as well be blind.
When dealing with men of ice, you don't have to be so nice,
And if that's freedom's price, we don't mind.

Strong lights played upon the folk singer who stood in

the customary place under the Minerva, singing the customary song that had been sung at Columbia, sung at Berkeley, sung in the South. A very large crowd, five thousand or more, looked up at the singer and came in strong on the line, "If that's freedom's price, we don't mind." From Ripon Hall's second floor, faces looked out and listened. They could hear, but they were too far away to see the local, liberal whities, the gray brothers, the ofay, maybe okay, cats do their thing.

It was ten o'clock at night. The rally had been going on for hours, with no drop in attendance. From time to time Shapiro or the Supreme Cream had taken the microphone to tell people not to go away, "There will be an action tonight." But there had also been plenty of entertainment, folk singers, a chain of contradictory speakers—all rising to clarify the issues—and a message from McVey that he would meet with everybody in Oberlin Auditorium immediately, or whenever they wanted. Much debate about this, resolved by sending an interrogatory message back to Fletcher Hall, asking if he would meet to negotiate the issues. These were now referred to as the black demands and the white demands, the latter being (1) agree to the black demands, (2) amnesty for the police car people, (3) the abolition of XXVII and unrestricted liberty of speech, and (4) Administration surrender of disciplinary powers to a joint commission. The message came back from Fletcher saying that McVey was anxious to "discuss" all "grievances." This language was denounced as a liberal, establishmentarian tactic designed to avoid talking about substantive questions while appearing reasonable to the public at large.

For the better part of an hour the crowd listened to the argument over tactics. The liberal majority thought it wouldn't hurt to go into Oberlin and hear what the chancellor had to say. The SDS-ers and the other radicals kept repeating it was a trick to keep them talking, get them off the Square and into Oberlin where McVey would divide them and confuse them until no action was possible. Then Tully Haskins came over from Ripon Hall and made a short speech in which he said the blacks were only interested in their demands, that they could go in and "socialize" with A. A. McVey anytime, and "you whites can do whatever you want, but if you want to help us, you'll do the same as us."

This swung a large part of the crowd back toward the radicals. It didn't end the meeting in a decision, because the radical leaders off to one side of the Minerva were quarreling among themselves. The split and the reasoning behind it were the same as at Rennecker Hall the day of the police car. Roger advocated support of the blacks, and the only way to do that was to seize a building. Shapiro argued that the crowd wasn't ready, instead they should march into Fletcher, as many as could fit in, confront McVey in person, and demand that he produce Hungerford and negotiate. Roger didn't like that, but he agreed to it when he realized it was now so late that most of the buildings were locked, except for the dorms. Seizing them would play into the Administration's hands by irritating the people who lived there. Fletcher was open, obviously, because McVey was in there.

Fletcher *was* open, but McVey wasn't in the building. He had left by a side exit to go to Rennecker for a brief meeting with the Dean of Students, his staff, and several police officials. Rennecker was chosen as the meeting place because several of the police officers were in uniform, and there was apprehension the sight of them on campus, going into Fletcher, might stir the crowd up.

Roger made the speech telling the people what the action was, and everybody began to move up the steps, into Fletcher to face McVey with the demand for negotiations.

It was one of Roger's better speeches. Under pressure from Shapiro and the others he used few dirty words. He recalled some of the phrases he had spoken to Ellie earlier, talking about an "artificially created, morally neutral, freezing cold universe. But I say there is a sun in this cosmos. I say that it warms our hearts and nourishes our souls. I say we are more than patterned particles, intervals in dead space tending toward absolute zero. I say we are men and we know we are men because we know what is good, we know what is beautiful, we know what is true and above all, we know what is RIGHT!!!"

The procession was almost soundless. After hundreds had entered Fletcher and the first-floor halls and corridors could hold no more, somebody on a power megaphone began whispering into it, "Turn right and go upstairs as you go in, as you go in turn right and go upstairs, no more room on the first floor."

The astronomer said, "It has a moving quality about it. Don't you think, Myron?" His voice was hoarse in the way people become dry-mouthed who have stood still not swallowing for a long time.

"Yes."

The two men were well back in the Square. Their position gave them a broad look going up the steps past the Minerva and through the doors. They could see many people now in the windows and catch the sounds of the people inside singing with a guitar player:

If I had a hammer, I'd hammer in the morning,
I'd hammer in the evening—all over this land.
I'd hammer out danger, I'd hammer out a warning,
I'd hammer out love between my brothers and sisters
    —all over this land.

"Myron, if you were their age, what would you do? Would you be inside with them?"

"I don't know. It goes deep against the training, what they're doing," Mirsky answered in a slow, reflective way, without his ordinary voluble bubble of words. "It's hard to say. Poets can write about youth as though it were always the same, always recurring with the same, wide, wild feelings, and perhaps it does sometimes. My youth was contingent on my times, who I was, a Jewish boy in a school my family couldn't afford to send me to. It was still one of your Wasp universities then, and I wanted to be an intellectual, savant, and in those days a savant was a man who equivocated passion, saw the grey areas, both sides of the question, all the qualities these young people despise intellectuals for. That was the dominating model of my youth—investigate and equivocate."

"But would you have gone into the building?"

"If Roger Elias had given a speech like that when I was going to school, he couldn't have held his audience. They wouldn't even have booed. They would have walked away. They would have said, 'simplistic demagogy.' If I were a young man today, I wouldn't be the same young man I was, so I can't answer your question. What would you have done, my friend the stargazer?"

"Oh, I would have gone into the building. I was on CIO picket lines and I heard a lot of simplistic demagogy then. I believed it."

"Well, of course you did. But, if instead of the demagogues talking about politics, what if they'd talked about the stars? Would you have believed it then?"

"No, I suppose not. Even then I was a student of the stars."

"And even then," Mirsky hastened to say, "I was a student of human behavior."

The two were silent for a minute, then the astronomer said, "Myron, I'm surprised. I assumed you'd be more sympathetic to what they're doing. I really would have thought that you'd have more to say than 'simplistic.' "

"I do."

"I'm surprised, too, that I have to ask you so many questions to get you going. Usually it's enough to bring up a topic to get an hour's free lecture."

"Well, my friend, now you get the free lecture," Myron said, and there was in the way he said it a tone which bespoke of getting down to business. "Something like this makes me stop, because it's serious for me personally. I tell you. When I was a young man, I sought out the rationalist interpretation of history. I liked people like Beard, people who would prove the Civil War was actually a battle over protective tariffs and government investment policies, or that the American Revolution was at best a mercantile quarrel. You know, Sam Adams did it for the money. This way you could step around the part that passion and belief play, subordinate them to a minor role, and when it was impossible to step around great, single acts of courage, which even a Machiavelli, or better, a Hobbes, wouldn't explain by money, you could fall back on fanaticism, deviant personality, psychic payoffs, that kind of analysis. It wasn't the fashion on the campus then, as you know, my friend, to go at big things strongly. . . . Have you ever read McVey's magnum opus? *Social Pluralism—Midway in the American Century?*

"No."

"Well, don't. It's out of date. Mr. Elias and his friends did that. It's sort of a Newtonian analysis of the American political system in which a great number of orderly forces, like organized capital, conveniently pour their energies into orderly machines which compromise all differences so everybody gets something of the goodies, and we're very happy. And I suppose a lot of us were until a few years ago, and the ones who weren't were invisible non-forces who had no effect on Dr. McVey's Newtonian machine. It was a very fine schema; he got a Pulitzer Prize for it. The only drawback is that it's wrong; it doesn't work because there's nothing in his system of perpetual haggling, 'trade-off' in his lingo, of 'here you take this and I get that,' between special-interest groups, there's nothing in all those pages to account for or deal with intransigent moral conviction, or passion, serene or angry.

"The social thinkers, my generation of them, so despised belief, we wrote books saying it was an anachronism, that it didn't exist anymore except among archaic Rights, true believers who wanted to fight socialism by getting rid of fluoridation. So now what is McVey going to do? I don't know. Under his system of analysis, Roger Elias either doesn't exist at all or he's clinically insane. But he isn't insane. He would be if he made that speech ten years ago, but tonight he had four or five thousand people agreeing with him, so he can't be insane. It's too bad you're not an astrologer. I would ask *you* questions."

"For instance?"

"What's McVey going to do? He had his chance to negotiate with the blacks, who are the kind of people who fit in his system, but now he has to come up against the blacks reinforced by the Eliases and the Shapiros."

The astronomer turned to look at Mirsky. "Then, Myron, you're back where you began. You don't think much of Elias."

"No, I do, but I'm frightened. How can I deal with Elias any better than McVey can? I'm a teacher here, a respected, I hope, member of the faculty. I have to deal with Elias, too, like you. I have some responsibility. But I can't do what I expect McVey is going to finish doing, which is to scream he's against all forms of extremism. That will put him in complete opposition to Elias, but it won't answer the question Elias' existence raises. What is wrong with our system of thinking? Millions of poor people and black people in this country, and we didn't see them. It took these meshugganah, these true-believing fanatics, these crazy

young people to find them; it took them to say to us, 'You
mean to tell us you old geezers are sane, practical men,
when you call peace everyone having a big bomb of his
own so everybody is afraid to use it?' But Elias is wrong,
too, and we have no way to deal with him, men like me,
equivocating men, who go slow and see both sides."

"I'm like that, Myron. I don't want to take sides."

"Oh, I'm afraid they'll make us. Well, us they won't, my
friend. Not you and me. We will take our own side; we will
try to save this place; we will try to remember there should
be no sides in a university, that the sides are our colleagues
and students. That's the star we must hold to, the star of
the University, a great, ancient corporate body of men who
love truth, McVey's kind and Elias' kind because truth is
detached, but it's not morally indifferent. We must mediate.
We must bring both understandings together."

As Mirsky spoke, both men heard a scraping, banging
noise off to the side, and turning in the direction of Manion
Gate they saw three policemen dragging sawhorses across
the main University entrance, turning it into a check-point,
sealing off the campus and the Square.

"God! New idiocy," Mirsky exclaimed.

From Fletcher Hall, now stuffed with people in and
around it, the folk song once more:

> I got a hammer and I got a bell;
> It's a hammer of justice, it's a bell of freedom . . .

VIII

MISCELLANY, DOCUMENTATION, AND INTELLIGENCE (*from around the time of Fletcher Hall's "Liberation"*)

The following document was taken by the police when Roger Elias' room was raided. The original, so far as is known, is still in the District Attorney's files. Since it was never used as evidence in any of the trials, no one knows why it was impounded. This version comes from a Xerox copy made by the police for Blackie McTavish. It has no page numbers; the order of the pages printed here was arranged by a radical faculty member, who edited the manuscript and prepared it for publication in a left-wing underground newspaper, where it appeared under the title "The Confessions of a White Middle-Class Revolutionary by Comrade Ex, Ph.D. and all that bullshit." The grounds for believing it was written by

*Roger are very strong, though there is nothing to indicate what
he had intended doing with these thoughts, written on lined,
five-and-dime store paper with a ballpoint pen. The rest of his
papers, shipped with his effects to his parents' house, contain
nothing like the notes. The unattributed quotes have been identified as coming from Georges Sorel. A copy of Sorel's Reflections on Violence was one of the few non-mathematical
books found in Roger's bare little room. Some of the sentences
in the notes are quite probably paraphrases of Sorel, the French
Marxist philosopher who died in 1922, having influenced such
diverse people as Wyndham Lewis and Benito Mussolini.*

Che! It makes me laugh to hear radicals complain about
the liberal–mass media explanation for Che's popularity with
people my age. Unthinking romantics they call us. Smitten
with the [illegible] of a dreamer. Or, they say, part of alienated youth's fantasy. I hear they are making a movie of
Che's life. I can imagine what that will be like. Romantic.
Not even an anti-communist propaganda thing. It will be an
absurd romantic odyssey. Like those cruddy Che wall
posters, twice as big as life, as large as W. C. Fields, Kim
Novak, Humphrey Bogart, or Bobby Kennedy. Hang it up
in your room, have it for your very own, lock the door,
smoke grass, listen to the music, put a sweet asshole smile
on your face.

Che! It's not youth that's romanticized Che. We haven't
needed to. It's the others, the old ones who are over thirty
and the young ones who were born over thirty. People who
use slang expressions like groovy and have the damn Che
posters on their bedroom walls because they say it blows
their parents' minds. I still laugh to hear radicals complain
of this sort of thing. They act like teen-agers. They act like
kids in the Che Guevara fan club when the top-forty dj
says he won't get a gold impression for his new record.

Che! The romanticization of Che is the ruling society's
protection against the meaning of Che. We will sell you Che

dolls, Che sweatshirts, but we will not show you Che's corpse in Vallegrande, the fly open, legs shattered, naked to the waist, blood, hair, rigid, dead eyes. That would make a good poster, a poster that would make people think, that would destroy romanticism.

Che! He was a hero. You are not supposed to say that. We don't call people heroes now, unless they are ballplayers, sports figures. Heroism and romanticism are opposed. American society won't tolerate heroes. The man on the street says the hero is corny. The literary critic says this is the age of the anti-hero. The hipster says Lenny Bruce is the only hero possible, sticking needles in himself, going crazy reading law books to beat the felonious lawyers at their own game. The hipster hero ODs and dies. Sophisticates think only the John Birch Society and the American Legion can take the ideal of heroism seriously. The most noble concept the American upper-class bourgeois can conceive of is "he was a brave man." In this formulation the brave man is somebody who dies according to the rules. A trudge [best reading] trudging, trudging, sad, doing his neat, crew-haircut best, dying with enough life insurance, a plodding, plastic stoic.

Che! The heroism of Che was that he didn't believe in circumstances. He believed in man and he believed you could change your life, you could change circumstances. He died trying to do that. He didn't accept being a fat-ass anti-hero. He didn't believe a turd like Willie Lohman was a great, big tragedy. He believed that to accept Willie Lohman as anything but a comic, miserable, gutless, despicable shit was to buy the self-pity, the pretty tenderness, the delicately cultivated bourgeois sense of powerlessness. Che did not believe man was powerless. He knew man can choose the time and place and method and meaning of his own death, and so man can never, never be powerless. We can ACT.

The scummy people who want to understand me say,

"Sonny, you really are an American. You think you are a radical, but you are saying just what our Founding Fathers said. They thought like you. They didn't believe this sociology bullshit about circumstances and environment. They believed like you in individual freedom and all of that. Sonny, you went to school and you believed what the teacher said about the Constitution and Lincoln and Jefferson. You took it seriously. Sonny, you are not a radical, you are a good old-fashioned American boy scout."

That is funky horseshit lying. I ask them in answer, "Where are your good old-fashioned modern living heroes? Why are all your heroes dead for a century? They cannot answer that. In the back of their mind they see the statues that are put up of modern-day bourgeois politicians with business suits covering fat stomachs. When the bourgeoisie stopped making statues of its heroes in phony Roman togas, it stopped producing them. It stopped having that capacity. Now what they have for heroes is Eisenhower and his doctors on TV telling us how many farts he had today, how rich and freedom-loving they smell.

If I had lived in Lincoln's time, I would have been Lincoln's man. I would have been Jefferson's man. I would have been Lenin's man, and that's why I'm Che's man. Oh, but they tell me I had a hero and he was killed in Dallas. No, I didn't. The man who was killed in Dallas is the romantic figure, the real romantic figure of my youth. It was not Che's tailor or his wife or his interior decorator that made him a hero. It was the conviction that he could make a revolution. I will not accept that mass-media confection for my hero.

Sometimes I want to puke. My father, that great trade-union leader, says to me, "What's the matter with you? I am a radical and I don't act like you. You don't have to act crazy to be a radical. You are worse than a commie." Did he ever suffer? Did he ever try to do anything but get his?

I look at him sometimes, and I want to take out my cock and pee on his leg. It's like having Lyndon Johnson or Hubert Humphrey or Richard Nixon or Averell Harriman or any of the great statesmen of mass media for your father. Pee on them, pee on the best of them.

I hate my father. He dares, damn him, to say he knows what I am feeling. He is against war, too, but "sometimes you got to fight." I am not against war. I am against his wars. Once he said to me that he wanted me to go into the union movement (what movement?). He was wearing a suit with a vest because he had looked at the corporate vice-presidents on the other side of his negotiating table and had seen they wore vests. But he does not play tennis, and his gut is too big for his vests. He said unions are a good business. He used the word "business." He said I should go to law school and then come home and go to work in the family union. I wanted to piss on his fat knee. I wanted to piss on his fat hand, the one he uses to bribe congressmen. I told him I was going to be a mathematician.

Sometimes I cannot believe how much of a temper I have. I don't understand where the anger comes from, but I'm glad I have it. If I didn't have it I would never have gotten out of our living room. I have been told to see a shrink. I would rather lose my balls than my anger. I might lose my balls with my anger. I would lose some sex appeal. I have sex appeal. That surprises me. I am ugly. It doesn't seem to matter with some women. I have noticed when I am giving a speech and I come to a pause, exhausted and catching my breath, I will close my eyes and open them to see a woman looking at me. I can tell she is excited.

My father accuses me of not having a plan. The word he uses is "program." He has memorized the clichés of liberalism. We are nihilists, negative, and criticism is destructive. Criticism is destructive, that is what criticism is. We are negative because we are against the system. We appear to him to be nihilists because we do not want to tinker with the system, we want to destroy it. He had a program. Like hell he did. He had a few suggestions for the people who run this country. The most manly thing I can say about my father is that he is a bandit, a man who betrayed the workers, his followers, to get the money to buy that living room which chokes me. Che had asthma. It's possible his father had a living room like mine that gave him asthma. I don't know why I don't have asthma. I cannot breathe in that man's house. I remember the day he told my mother to take the transparent plastic off the living room upholstery. But then, she said, the couch and the armchair will get dirty. My father said when that happens you are supposed— he used the word supposed—to have it sent out and recovered. He learned that from the bosses, the enemy, the opposition, how to dress, how to keep the furniture in the living room. I was little then, when the plastic left the living room and we didn't eat at the kitchen table with the oilcloth cover. My mother had better motives, but he ruined her. She plays bridge, as much bridge as any coed in this fucking university.

Marx said, "The man who draws up a programme for the future is a reactionary" (my father). He thought the proletariat had no need to take lessons from the learned inventors of solutions to social problems, which is true, which is true. You close *their* university, stop it, [illegible] it, and you make it free, libro, libre, frei, free, free, free, and the program comes. The radical faculty, the students begin with their university, shaping it, making it in accordance with their needs, not the needs of GM or whoever, Incorporated, for engineers, or those barfing stinking individuals who are called well-rounded liberal-arts shits, the types that are supposed to have the broad, general, upper-middle-class training to step in and do anything, run a steel company, a university, a battleship, a counter-insurgency. That's what the blacks did at San Francisco State College. [Evidently this portion of the document was written before Afro Day at the University or surely Comrade Ex would have mentioned it.—ED.]

All plans, programs, and utopias are anti-revolutionary. Half of the crap people call plans—at least the ones radicals argue about—are a verbose fighting over booty that has not been won yet. When the revolution comes we shall do this, and they shall get that. The establishment has nothing to fear from programs and utopias. That is why they tax us for not having them. The slob Humphrey always had a plan for something or other drooling out of his mouth, and the most reactionary people in America, the bankers and the labor leaders, wanted to make him president.

When a radical is asked, the way they always ask, what do you propose to do, the answer should always be, make a revolution. Then they ask, but what are you going to do after the revolution? The proper answer is, the revolution I will help make will decide that. What inspires people is the thought of the REVOLUTION. Making the revolution is the plan, the liberating and uplifting force. The rest is contemptible. You can say our plan is to see everyone has a Buick, or the dean of students will not be elected, or we are going to have the pass/fail system, or community-controlled police forces. All that shit is a distraction. What matters is the belief that in the revolution man makes his own circumstances; that we rise, we become better and generous and fraternal and we sacrifice for each other and hope to be heroes.

If someone read some of the things I have written, he might say that sonny boy is revolting against his father, he is inflicting his oedipal struggle on the society at large. I would say that someone sucks. I am not in rebellion against what my father preaches. I am revolting against his not practicing it. I am a dutiful son. He is a betraying father. My mother suffers ignorantly.

The revolution is utopian. The revolution will make itself

when the contradictions in the system cause it. One must not make a revolution until the objective circumstances are right. They were right in Cuba in 1958, so Fidel and Che made the revolution. They were wrong in Bolivia in 1967, and Che was captured and murdered.

This is obscurantist shit. The revolution is the one thing that is real. In the universities and the ghettos, and it is beginning in the armed services. These rebellions are happening. They are concrete, actual. Che has said the truth already. He said, "We need not always wait for all the revolutionary conditions to be present; the insurrection itself can create them." Shapiro cannot understand this. He is a professor, basically. He believes in science, not man. He is looking for revolutionary conditions like a man reading gauges on a laboratory apparatus. I tell him our revolt will make revolutionaries. He says he doesn't want to be a martyr. To die like Che.

To die like Che. How did he die? So he failed. He chose the meaning of his death. Hungry, hunted, wheezing probably, he had no medicine, troops trained by our government closing in on him, shot in the leg, crawling up a hill and getting captured. But they had not killed him, thirsty, covered with insect bites, because he put the meaning on his life and his death.

To die like Che. No. Heroism does not look for death. It accepts death as a risk. I had a putrid, necrophiliac girl up here one night. She said she wanted me to lay her because she could feel I was like Che. She said I should grow a beard like him. I told her to go to a morgue and fuck a dead man. She told me if I went into her I would change into a dead body and she could predict how I would die. I told her to get out.

I saw her on campus recently. She formed some words with her lips but made no sounds. She convinces me the actual fact of the revolution is too much for some people to take. They know if they allow the idea to penetrate them they will come into a sublime, spiritual condition. That will strain them. Instead, they postpone like Shapiro, or they destroy themselves on perversions. Fucking a dead man is better than risking life. So they think.

I have trouble finding the right woman. Because I cannot find the right one, I have many. I don't go looking for them. They come to me. Some girls have even walked over here at night to have me sleep with them. I think they want me to screw them because they believe I'm violent. Personally, I am not violent. They are violent, and they are part of a reeking, violent society. They think violence is masculine, so they come to get fucked by me. Before there were revolutionaries like me on campus, this type probably spread their legs for football players, but now they have given up the amateur violence of sports for what they think is the murderous violence of politics. These same women will tell their sons they are cowards if they resist fighting in some future neo-colonial American war.

In politics I believe in violence. The blacks have shown the way here. They became a revolutionary and growing force when they became violent. Violence for the revolution convinces them that black is beautiful, truly so. It makes them anti-patriotic. They have their own revolutionary war to fight. The most important thing it does is separate the races. It makes irremediable cleavage. It creates a condition where every white man reacts to every black man as his probable killer. This alienates more black men because of the treatment they get from these frightened whites, and it makes recruits for the black revolutionary cause. The slightest incidents of daily life are now symptoms of the state of revolutionary race war. This creates an atmosphere of catastrophe and pessimism and doom which destroys the work of the sowers of unity, the ameliorists. It robs liberals of their faith in fucking progress based on consensus, the whole demeaning philosophy of "move over and give this new guy a tit to suck on." Violence does that. Violence makes cleavage and polarization. It makes the black man know he is black. It makes the liberal know he is at heart an establishmentarian reactionary. Violence recruits for the revolution, and with greater violence the revolution wins.

The same process is working with college students. Violence teaches them who they are, too. It destroys the manipulative myth of the academic community. Community is impossible. The administration and half the faculty are afraid of assault from minute to minute. They must live on the *qui vive*. They must develop the nervous spot on the brain missionaries must have. They must ask themselves, will these people put me in a pot and eat me before I can civilize them? Civilize is a word meaning psychologically subjugate, coopt, brainwash, or turn into whoring stooges—our student government—anyone who agrees to serve a humiliating apprenticeship—eat shit is what it really is—during the time they hang around for the payoff. Violence forces the Administration to use counter-violence. That visibly establishes what the true relationship between the students and the Administration is.

Violence is educational. Even low-level violence, like sitting in on a draft board, instructs the little religious, pacifist ones, because the Selective Service system retaliates against them. Violence creates the psychology in the older people that the sons are going to ravish their mothers. All bases of confidence between groups are ruined by violence. Revolutionary violence is our means of attaining heroism. We must have violence on this campus. We are way behind others. Berkeley, the University of Oregon, Michigan, Columbia, San Francisco State. They have had fighting, shooting and bombing. Here? Nothing yet.

I have just read some of the paragraphs on violence. I can see that if someone read them who did not know me, they could conclude I was a pretty violent person. I am not. I'm gentle. Personally, I do not like violence. To die like Che? No, but I must elevate my life. I will become violent if I accept the circumstances of my life. I would be violent if I did. I would not be gentle. I would accept the thrill-seeking women, be violent to them, and fuck. I accept the possibility of dying like Che, but I hope to live, be gentle and lift up my life and give it meaning.

The Metropolitan Press:

VIOLENCE, SIT-INS GROW AT U
Police Called After Arson Try

Students seized two more buildings at the University's main campus last night after youthful black-power militants ran amuck on the Square, beating people and attempting to burn down at least two buildings. At 11:30 last night, after hours of turmoil, 300 city police sealed off the campus, although they did not enter the University itself.

A University spokesman said the campus was sealed off because the trouble was caused mostly by non-students. He said the University is functioning normally today and that all employees, teachers, students and legitimate visitors would be passed through police barricades at the main entrances.

The trouble began in the afternoon when Negro students who seized Ripon Hall two days ago held a black-power celebration in the Square. It began peacefully but soon degenerated into a mob action with several hundred militants attacking white students and faculty, apparently at random. Flexner Research Hospital and nearby Saint Boniface's reported treating five people, who were later released. One newspaper cameraman had his film taken from him.

Later yesterday a crowd of 2,000 to 3,000 students assembled in front of Fletcher Hall, the University's main administration building, to support the black students and demand immediate changes in a number of University rules. At about 11 P.M. they stormed the building and occupied it. Sometime afterward, at approximately 3 A.M., another group broke into Philosophy Hall and seized it.

Asked why the police made no attempt to stop the militants, Deputy Inspector Joe Manfried, Chief of Uniform Patrol, said, "The University is a private institution. We can't go on their property unless we actually see a crime in progress. They felt they could handle it better on their own." Manfried refused to comment on whether the police should have been called onto the campus itself.

At a press conference this morning, University Chancellor A. A. McVey, Jr., said, "Any university is extremely reluctant to bring police onto its campus. After consultation with police authorities and people in the Mayor's office about any possible racial overtones, it was felt that it would be in the best interests of all not to ask the police to intervene at that time. During the course of the night, particularly after the seizure of Fletcher Hall, it became apparent that a large number of non-students were participating and perhaps guiding these demonstrations. That is why we closed the campus to the general public. This is a temporary measure. Only a minority of those involved are students, according to our best information, and as soon as they are out of the picture the disturbances will subside and we will be able to deal with our own family disagreements in an orderly fashion."

Roger Elias, spokesman for the dissidents, said, "That's a lot of hogwash. It is what you would expect . . ."

Editorial in the right-wing metropolitan tabloid:

FIRST SAVIO, THEN RUDD, NOW ELIAS

The suburban Red Guard has struck at the University.

President Martin Hungerford and Chancellor A. A. McVey, Jr., shouldn't feel bad about it. It's not due to anything they've done. The University was on SDS's list. Reliable information has it that at a secret SDS meeting held last summer in Des Moines, Iowa, it was decided that after having decimated Berkeley and Columbia the radicals would attack here. Our local street-corner loudmouth is even more slovenly of mind and subversive of intent than Mario Savio of Free (?) Speech Movement fame or Mark Rudd, the Maoist-Castroite who planted the red flag at Columbia.

We hope that the University administration doesn't think this is a time to be permissive and understanding. We understand Roger Elias and we don't think he should be permitted . . . to attend school there or walk free on the streets. This whole mess could be ended by throwing about four people in jail or perhaps a good, old-fashioned leather-belt session in the woodshed would do.

Letter to tabloid editor:

Dear Sir:

I am a University alumnus, Class of '44. I am sick of the conduct of the students and the cowardly vacillation of the President and the Board of Trustees who should have expelled this bunch of rotten apples weeks ago. I'm sending back my sheepskin and selling my class ring.

Glum Alum

OFFICIAL POLICE DEPARTMENT TRANSCRIPT OF TAPPED CONVERSATIONS ON SHAPIRO'S PHONE THE DAY AFTER FLETCHER HALL (Subject made no calls and received only two in this twenty-four-hour period. His roommate made one to his doctor, who checks out.—R. Murriello, Badge No. 3126)

1331 Hours

SUBJECT: Hello.

FEMALE VOICE: Can I speak to Howie?

SUBJECT: He isn't here.

FEMALE VOICE: Ray? This's Shirley. When's he coming back?

SUBJECT: I don't know. I just got in a couple of hours ago—trying to get a little sleep. He wasn't here.

FEMALE VOICE: God, I've just gotta find him. Could you do me a favor, Ray?

SUBJECT: Well, I'm pretty busy and I need to get some sleep. You know all the stuff that's happening.

FEMALE VOICE: I think it's marvelous. Did you know you were on television this morning? I'm really impressed. A celebrity.

SUBJECT: Thanks, Shirley.

FEMALE VOICE: Ray, I don't like to ask you with the revolution and all, but you could do me a small favor. I'm afraid Howie won't get back. Ray, could you look to see if I left my pills there?

SUBJECT: What do they look like?

FEMALE VOICE: They're the round kind. I mean, they come in the round plastic case. You know, you move it around in the circle, one for each day of the month.

SUBJECT: Okay. Wait.

FEMALE VOICE: You're a dear, even if everybody says you're crazy.

SUBJECT: Hello.

FEMALE VOICE: Ray?

SUBJECT: Yeah. I can't find them.

FEMALE VOICE: Oh, God, what am I going to do?

SUBJECT: Buy some more.

FEMALE VOICE: I've got to get a prescription, and I can't do it today. If you skip a day you have to start all over.

SUBJECT: So start all over, Shirley.

FEMALE VOICE: That means Howie will have to use—you know what I mean—for a whole month.

SUBJECT: Oh.

FEMALE VOICE: Oh well, maybe they're here. I'll look again.

SUBJECT: Hope you find them.

FEMALE VOICE: Thanks. Oh, and good luck with the revolution. Will you be on TV tonight?

SUBJECT: I don't know. Goodbye, Shirley.

FEMALE VOICE: Goodybe, Ray.

1908 Hours

SUBJECT: Hello.

FEMALE VOICE: Raymond, is that you? My God, we've been so worried. You don't know. We saw it all on Huntley-Brinkley. What a thing! Are you all right? We're worrying our hearts out for you, Raymond. Those blacks! They had them on, too. I wouldn't have believed it. I don't know what to say. It's terrible. Your Aunt called. She couldn't believe it. She and Harry saw it on Walter Cronkite. It was worse on CBS. She didn't know what to say. My God! Who'd have believed it?

SUBJECT: Hello, Mother.

FEMALE VOICE: That's all? Hello, Mother?

SUBJECT: You were lucky to get me. I just walked in the door to get something and heard the phone ring.

FEMALE VOICE: Don't you ask me how I am?

SUBJECT: Sure. How are you?

FEMALE VOICE: Terrible. Tomorrow the whole neighborhood'll think you're a communist, a pinko.

SUBJECT: That's all right. Don't worry about it.

FEMALE VOICE: I live here. It's not all right. What am I going to say? My God! I can hear it already. The neighbors, the man at the checkout counter, "I saw your son on TV." That's all they'll say, but you know what they're thinking. Raymond Shapiro's a pinko. My son.

SUBJECT: Well, I guess in a way I *am* a pinko. So?

FEMALE VOICE: You're an American. Your Dad was in the Second World War. My father was in the First World War. You're an American, Raymond. Not a pinko. Don't say pinko. I want you to promise me. Never say pinko again. Don't even think pinko. What? Yes. No, wait. All right. Your Dad wants to talk to you.

MALE VOICE: You all right, Ray?

SUBJECT: Yeah, Dad. How're you?

MALE VOICE: It's you I'm worried about. Don't you think you're being pretty idealistic? Just from what I heard on the television, it sounded like that. Pretty militant, you know.

SUBJECT: I guess.

MALE VOICE: Son, what does this do to your marks? You know, getting your degree?

SUBJECT: I'm through here unless we win.

MALE VOICE: Unless you win you're through? You know what I always say, son, it's good to have the degree just in case.

SUBJECT: We'll have to see what happens.

MALE VOICE: Couldn't you talk to someone? One of your teachers? Or the dean, maybe?

SUBJECT: Dad, we're having a revolution.

MALE VOICE: That's what it looked like on Huntley-Brinkley tonight. A regular revolution. Son, I didn't think much of those Negroes. Is that a way for them to behave? You know, it's a university, not Bull Connor or Mayor Daley. I'm for their rights, you know that, but are they going to turn the University into another Watts?

SUBJECT: Dad, that's where black people are at right now.

MALE VOICE: You could get hurt. Can't you get out of this thing? I'm afraid it's going to hurt you later on in life.

SUBJECT: I'm one of the leaders, Dad.

MALE VOICE: Yeah, that's what it looked like on Huntley-Brinkley tonight.

SUBJECT: We need a revolution in this country. Things have got to change.

MALE VOICE: I believe in you. You know that, son, but you're a young man. I wouldn't like to see your future spoiled. You know, when you get to be forty, sometimes, well, you may feel the same way, but there're considerations in life. I wouldn't like to see you do something you'd be sorry for later. You know, you can only be so much of an idealist.

SUBJECT: I gotta go, Dad. Say goodbye to Mother for me.

MALE VOICE: We're in your corner, Ray, no matter. Don't be afraid to call. I'm not afraid of trouble. We've had trouble in this family before. Call. I want to hear from you. Don't forget your parents. Your mother worries. It's a shock to see your own son on Huntley-Brinkley.

SUBJECT: Dad, thanks, but I gotta go. I gotta say goodbye. Goodbye, Dad.

MALE VOICE: Son, don't be afraid to call. We love you. We'll stand by you. We love you, son. Hear Ray? No, no. He had to go. He said goodbye. Ray? No. I told you. He's in a revolution, what do you—

TEXT OF A PAID ADVERTISEMENT IN THE DAILY REVIEW

Experience having taught me that all newspapers must misquote whomever they interview, I buy my own space when I want to speak to the community. As one who has, much against my will, been drawn into the center of the strife which has divided this University and threatens to destroy it altogether, it is necessary that all be given an opportunity to know my true opinion and belief lest, by misunderstanding, what is already awful with us be made worse.

A demand has been made by an organization describing itself as representative of the University's Negro students that I cease teaching my *Foundations of Western Civilization* course. It is alleged that in it I propagate, albeit "institutionally" and therefore unknowingly, racist attitudes and opinions. Although denials of such accusations are unseemly and self-serving, and thereby received skeptically by practical men, the charges are so serious and grievous that I do publicly deny them absolutely, completely, unqualifiedly, and without reservation.

Supposing, however, they were true, I believe this University would commit moral suicide, would dishonor itself and separate itself from learning, scholarship, and letters if it were to accede to this demand. I could say this on the grounds that no institution can permit itself to be coerced by violence into dismissing a professor; I could say this on the grounds that once this were done, the way would be open for the changing of the University into a school run on the model of those found in South America and Japan, where faculties are hired and fired not by virtue of their learning nor their dedication to disinterested truth but by their success or failure to model themselves on the political opinions prevailing among their students. This is oligarchy.

Yet it is not on these grounds I resist the demands, that I will have to be carried out of my classroom dead. No, I will resist because the test of truth is not force; the answer to error is not the gagging or banishment or the suppression of he who may speak in error. The answer to error is truth. It has always been thus, save only during those periods in the history of our civilization when we have given ourselves over to barbarism. If I be in error, let it be shown; let others come forth and teach what they believe to be the truth.

I realize that there are a few, younger faculty members for the most part, who agree with those who are trying to drive me from my classroom. I wish to remind them that it has taken centuries to secure the learned man immunity from reprisals for his unpopular ideas. In times past the passion to censor the teacher in his classroom has flamed brightest in breasts of those outside the academy. Need I recall the late Senator from Wisconsin, Joseph McCarthy? Did we repel him only to be overwhelmed from within by our own students?

In the past few days we have watched and taken part in the spreading destruction of customs and rules by which we have lived together and worked together in the course of pursuing man's highest callings. Every hour sees more of us, teachers and students alike, drawn to taking sides in what resembles a war more than a dispute.

Many of us have cause to be disturbed, to be unhappy, fretful, and angry with the University. I am, certainly. I, perhaps for different reasons, believe like Mr. Elias that the University is perverting, twisting, and destroying itself by becoming a great research and development laboratory for the Army and Navy or for the automobile industry or the pharmaceutical industry. That is not our work. I am as dismayed as anyone now entrenching himself in Ripon or Fletcher halls at our publishing-or-perishing, at our running about the entire globe selling our services to commercial organizations and governments, at our putting the interests of our students second to the writing and disseminating of repetitious drivel, at our preposterous degree-chasing, at our pretensions, at our arrogance, at our greed.

I believe we must return the University to being the disinterested haven of truth it once was, to being a place of contemplation, of the arts and sciences and other learned pursuits which are truly liberal. Ultimata published by young men who practice appearing sinister and menacing will not save the University. These young Negroes, eyes hidden behind smoked glass, rehearsing the roles of thugs and hooligans! These young whites, imbued with the revolutionary mystique, speaking fiery sedition! Will they save this University?

I ask you that. If you answer, faculty and student body, as people both idealistic and prudent, we will not have a

Columbia, or perhaps worse, here. There is still time.

ELDON RUSSELL, JR.

LETTERS TO THE DAILY REVIEW

The poll recently conducted by the Student Council shows that there is great support for protesters' demands but massive rejection for the means they have used to win them. Many more people voted in this poll than usually take part in these attempts to survey campus opinion.

Generally Favor Black Demands:
Yes: 4,211 (66%)
No: 1,693 (27%)
Don't Know: 417 (7%)
Favor Ripon Hall Sit-In:
Yes: 2,543 (40%)
No: 3,558 (56%)
Don't Know: 220 (4%)
Favor White Demands:
Yes: 3,975 (63%)
No: 1,996 (32%)
Don't Know: 318 (5%)
Favor White Tactics (Fletcher and Philosophy Hall Sit-Ins):
Yes: 1,028 (17%)
No: 4,314 (71%)
Don't Know: 747 (12%)

These figures show that most people would like to see change accomplished in an orderly and legal fashion. We all owe the protesters a debt of gratitude for focusing and dramatizing the issues, but now the time has come for the entire student body to put its weight behind the Council, which has voted to support both the black and white demands. No further purpose will be served by continuing the sit-ins.

LEONARD TRUAX, President, Student Council

I am writing as a mother of a member of the Class of
'73. I think the young people who are causing the revolution should remember how inexperienced they are. Ern-
esto "Che" Guevara, who seems to be a hero to many of
the students who are protesting, did not become a revolutionary until after he finished his education. In other words,
he completed his training and medical doctor's degree
before he tried to overthrow his first government. This
was wise because it meant he prepared himself for his life's
work. I think the young people at the University should
do the same if they really want to follow in his footsteps.

(Mrs.) Stephanie Williamson
LaJolla, California

(We checked this one out as best we could. Apparently it
is not a put-on.—EDS.)

ALL POWER TO THE IMAGINATION
(*painted on Mitchell Library wall*)

FEDERAL DISTRICT COURT
PRE-SENTENCE INVESTIGATION AND REPORT

DOCKET #2028815126
JUDGE: Wallace Bea
PRISONER: Morton Ellis Cream/oka The Supreme Cream
STATUS: Bail pending appeal
INVESTIGATING OFFICER: C. Roy Katcavic, MSW
(*The following in longhand was attached with paper clip to
the report:* Took this one personally to see if I could relate
to and communicate with a "political." My first such case.
Was curious.—CRK)

Morton is 23 years old. The University is the third college
he has attended. His marks are average. He is vague as to
why he dropped out of Princeton, then Rutgers, or came to

this city to attend college. He has had all the advantages our society can provide. His father is a member of the New York Stock Exchange. There is one other child in the family, a brother who is an executive of a steel company. His parents were divorced and remarried when he was fourteen. He reports he gets along well with them and his stepmother and stepfather. They agree, but the family does not appear to be close.

Morton has been a sympathizer with radical causes for a long time according to his family. He is evasive and unwilling to supply detailed information on his associates. From his family, who do not agree with him in what he did, it was learned that Morton had participated with the Student Non-Violent Coordinating Committee in Mississippi as a high school student and once again in several places in rural southwest Georgia. Information supplied by the Bureau indicates Morton took part in the radical assault on the Pentagon in 1967. He does not appear to have been a ringleader in any of these places. Morton has been pleasant but not helpful in disclosing his true role, if any. He did say some of his friends have referred to him as a "left-wing beach boy," "a radical surfer," and a "Marxist bum."

This delineation of Morton may be rather insightful. His college record indicates an inability to fix his goals and pursue them. At the three colleges he has attended, Morton has had three majors: geology, history, and English. This may account for his slow progress and evident lack of enthusiasm for his work. He expressed no anxiety about his failure to follow through on projects once started.

When asked to face up to this failure to develop goal-orientedness, Morton stated that he was able to complete tasks which interested him. He said he worked hard at gymnastics, had been a varsity man on the gymnastics team at all three colleges, and hoped to compete in the next Olympics. He seemed surprised when he was told that

America would probably not like to have an individual represent it who was a convicted felon, a person who had burned his draft card and done other unpatriotic things. I probed his surprise and am convinced it had not occurred to him he would be ineligible to represent his country. Several times he asked me, "Am I a felon?" or words to that effect.

As a person who had the advantages of a very advantaged childhood, Morton grew up overprotected, so that he does not have a realistic understanding of the consequences of his acts. His father and his family have seen him through prior difficulties and evidently he thinks parental intervention will occur again. His family has done little to discourage this attitude in Morton. Although his father stated strong disagreement with what his son had done, he gave an implied approbation of wrongdoing by saying that Morton had been brought up to do what he thinks is right, and he thinks burning his draft card is right. The father's behavior, even after the conviction, is highly supportive of Morton as he has continued to send his son an allowance and said he would do so after he is released from the penitentiary.

The father relates to Morton through guilty feelings which express themselves by overindulgence. The father feels guilty about his divorce from Morton's mother, stating that Morton's older male sibling had the advantage of reaching adulthood while the family was still together. This father-son relationship has encouraged Morton in an irresponsible, unthinking attitude which has bred a thoughtlessness about the obligations he owes other individuals or the community at large, a lack of public regardingness. It has helped induce in Morton a narcissistic life-style exemplified by an excessive concern for his body. His sports activities accordingly are not other-related or competitive, preferring ring gymnastics, body-building, and surfing.

The father's guilt has given rise to a compensatory protectiveness that has arrested Morton's emotional development, preventing him from having the other-related experience which heterosexuality provides. Morton has refused to compete with his father for his mother and therefore for other females. Instead, he has remained in a state of infancy that prevents him from understanding right from wrong in a grownup way. He has internalized childhood moral injunctions, knows it is wrong to lie or take other people's possessions, but he is unable, for example, to distinguish between the soldier's duty to the extended community—that is, his country—to fight, and what Morton persistently calls "killing people."

No amount of explanation appears to be able to help Morton internalize the difference. When he is told that fighting for your country is not killing or murder if the President and the Congress say it is your duty, he is still unable to relate this to his own obligation to bear arms. Nor can he use authority figures like the President to resolve his internal confusions. Given his indulgent father and his father's permissive, unstructured attitude to ethical questions, it is not surprising that Morton will not respond to authority figures outside the home.

Legally, Morton is sane. Clinically, he needs help. Without it the prognosis for rehabilitation is not good. I suggested to Morton that if he would be willing to volunteer for the armed forces, it was possible the court would suspend sentence, but he refused. He repeated his objection to being part of "murder," but when I questioned him carefully to determine if this objection was related to some recognized religio-ethical system, he was characteristically vague in his response. I repeated to him that he was in serious trouble and would certainly be sent to the penitentiary. He blocked, choosing to avoid reality, and remained in his self-related, narcissistic infant world. "I will never go to jail," he stated, which I took to mean that he clung to the belief his father would rescue him. If the defendant's sentence is suspended, all the indices suggest with the strongest degree of probability that he would commit the same crime again. Morton denies this. He stated, "How could I? They only give you one draft card, don't they?" (his exact words).

Text of telegram to Martin Hungerford:

URGE YOU MAKE NO CONCESSIONS. YOURS IS LOCAL BATTLE IN NATIONAL-INTERNATIONAL CONDITION THAT MUST BE DAMPED DOWN. SITUATION ON OUR AND MANY OTHER CAMPUSES TEETERING ON WHAT HAPPENS WITH YOU. SURE YOU SEE IMPORTANCE OF DEMONSTRATING PAST DOUBT COERCION, MOB ACTION NOT TO BE TOLERATED BY AMERICA'S UNIVERSITIES AND COLLEGES. STAND READY TO GIVE ANY SUPPORT WANTED OF ME, PUBLIC STATEMENTS, SPEECHES, JOINT DECLARATION BY HEADS OF BIG SCHOOLS. ALL OF US BACKING YOUR FIRM LEADERSHIP. REGARDS AND BEST WISHES.

ABLE CATLEDGE LOWERY,

PRESIDENT, ALBERT SCHWEITZER UNIVERSITY

Posted on Wall of Nexus (Revolutionary HQ) Office:

"That miserable, mumbling, slick, mendacious, wriggling, corrupted, and corrupting liberal press."

Leon Trotsky, Dec., 1904.

POLICE DEPARTMENT, COUNTER INTELLIGENCE UNIT

MEMORANDUM TO: Lt. R. C. McAndrews, Commanding
FROM: Pvt. T. P. Lukens, Badge No. 1119
CONCERNING: Undercover Surveillance of University Subversive Leaders
The leaders are certain I am one of them. I was in on the

Fletcher Hall seizure and was up with them when they broke into Philosophy Hall. The fact that I have been a part-time student at the University for several years is helpful.

There are two or three splits in Nexus. I have joined the most radical or Maoist faction, which is led by Roger Elias. The conservative or "Russian" faction is headed by Raymond Shapiro. A moderate faction appears disorganized and without a leader at this time. It is said to be stronger inside the two white-held buildings than at Nexus headquarters. There is no black leadership at Nexus. Both Elias and Shapiro are said to be in contact with the blacks. The Russian and Maoist factions claim to have black backing.

The factions have the same overall objectives but disagree on tactics. The Maoists are more for a fight to the death, and the Russians argue for winning a partial victory, which would allow them to get their sympathizers into key positions in the University. Both factions are aiming at destroying the United States government base in the University, putting a stop to all defense research and other government programs.

No hard information yet on firearms in the buildings. A lot of talk about resistance if a move is made to take them. I do not want to be too eager.

Shapiro and Elias have new foreign contacts. Maybe French. They have talked a lot about the French movement. They say a move will be made to start rebellions in the ghetto and in white factories. Their plan is to coordinate these uprisings with the University after they have taken over. They are showing people an article that spells it out and suggests plans are being made to hit other universities very soon:

". . . We must think of orienting our own movement in a way that more clearly makes the connections with working-class interests. For this to be done, 'exemplary actions' (e.g., we seize the universities, which implies our commitment to their seizure of the factories) are not sufficient unless there is already a common political framework. . . . The 'seizure' of the university should expropriate social resources for all who created them and against whom they function."

This comes from an article which appeared in the radical *Guardian* newspaper. It was written by Lewis Cole, Dave Gilbert, and Juan Gonzales. Identification Division says the three were ringleaders at Columbia. They have not appeared here as yet, but the article is mentioned a lot, although what plans for implementation and execution Elias and Shapiro have have not been disclosed.

We should be alert for a new element that appears to be very dangerous and may move at any time. This is a radical, anarchist faction. The leader of this faction is "Sil." He is only known by this alias. He is a white man in his early twenties, 6'2", 175 lbs., black hair, very long, curly bearded (black), blue eyes, unkempt, dirty appearance, no fixed abode or visible source of income. He heads a group with the code name of Fuckheads. He let slip on more than one occasion that this is a guerrilla group. Sil is the most difficult to gain the confidence of, which I do not have at the present time. On more than one occasion he has called me a "fink" and accused me of being a CIA agent. I laughed it off. As did others. His suspicions have not yet been allayed. I must be careful about asking too many questions about him. I do not believe he has any particular reason for thinking I am a police officer, but I may have betrayed myself in some small way.

Sil is a narcotics user. He carries marijuana on his person much of the time. He will smoke it in public and semi-public. He was told by Elias and Shapiro and others that he was not to do so at Nexus, and he appears to have stopped at the present time.

At this time his mission is a bomb attempt. He has talked about it in the Nexus headquarters three times. It is to be very large according to his description. Apparently to avoid incrimination, Shapiro has told him he is not to talk about it and that he is too busy to listen and does not want to hear about the bomb. Sil is closely allied with the Russian faction at the present time and obeys these instructions. I have not, because of this, been able to learn where the bomb or bombs are being built, type of design or explosives to be used. Sil has not indicated the target, but it will probably be somewhere on the campus. Others at Nexus have also spoken about dynamite, which they say can be purchased for $3 a stick. These plans are not as far advanced.

LETTER TO THE EDITOR OF THE DAILY REVIEW

Your cop-out editorial of the day before yesterday must be shot down immediately. Only the silliest kind of liberal could say at this point in a revolutionary upheaval that we are suffering from a communications failure. Men do not raise the red flag of revolution because they don't understand each other. Each side at this University fights because it *does* understand the other. We understand this Administration completely and that's why we refuse to recognize it as legitimate and why the students will destroy it and the kind of subservient liberal student press that could be asinine enough to propose a joint fact-finding commission at a time like this.

Up against the wall with you cop-outs too.

JOHN COMMINGS, SDS and class of '70, which I doubt will have a University to graduate from.

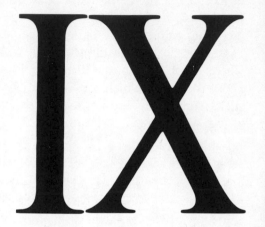

IX

Ellie gave out a gasping, nervous shriek of fatigue and surprise. She was standing looking at Sil's lynched Negro. It seemed more real in the night, in this quiet part of the campus. When she recognized what it was, she said, "Damn," and started walking toward her room again, but then she stopped and stared at the murdered man. Behind was the noise of people from the vicinity of Fletcher and Philosophy still running around, shouting and doing things, and it was nearly dawn. The buildings were being barricaded.

Without saying anything, Ellie had listened to the discussions leading to the decision to take Philosophy. Fletcher was overcrowded and the Administration would have more trouble pulling people out of two buildings than one. She had gone with them in excitement to Philosophy, watched them break the lock, and she would still be there if the two policemen hadn't come out of the air and caused a panic. Roger losing his head, telling people to jump out the windows, and Shapiro telling him he was a fool, they had to stay. Ellie had left in confusion, unprepared to be arrested, realizing she wanted to be arrested only after proper meditation. She needed to prepare her soul. And she was tired and overcome by the disorder of events and people.

In her room she took off her dress and stopped to listen to the chirping of birds, irritable, impatient sounds signaling the coming of dawn. Ellie went to the closet, climbed up on a suitcase, and from a shoe box got a small pouch tied with a silk ribbon and the small woman's pipe with a cut-glass diamond in it, which she filled. She lit it, inhaled the smoke, and kept it in her lungs until she'd crossed the room to sit by the windows and her eyes had begun to water and her head fuzz up. Then she released the smoke and looked out at the dull glow of urban horizon in the last minutes of night. Below her window she could see police vans and helmets in the bluish illumination of the vapor lights. She took another puff on her pipe and felt with mild surprise the quick effect of the smoke. Ellie remembered she hadn't eaten since breakfast the morning before.

"Can I have a puff?" her roommate asked, wiggling on down to the end of the bed near the window and holding her hand out. Ellie, watching the first start of a calm and purple dawn, handed over the pipe while she had a lazy debate with herself about the need, the wisdom, the advisability of shifting the debris of experience which had piled up in her head.

"I thought maybe you'd spend the night over there," the roommate said, handing the pipe back, "I was hoping you'd come back . . . I saw some cops beat up a boy."

"I saw a lynched Negro."

"You what?"

"Oh no, it wasn't really. It just looked that way."

"Could I have the pipe again?" Ellie returned it to the

other girl, who said, "I really did see two cops beat up a boy. Ellie, he just wanted to get into the Square and he didn't have his ID, so they wouldn't let him."

Ellie's head was a park after a picnic. She felt she ought to straighten it up, but she needed help taking the dead Negroes off the trees, sweeping up the words. People should be careful when they talk and not spill, or else they ought to clean up when they've finished speaking and put the containers in trash baskets. That's what they're for. There were even spots where words had been spilled and stained on Ellie's skirt.

"He'd gone out to get a pizza and he'd forgotten his ID. He had the pizza with him."

Sil was thoughtless. There were no containers for the Negroes, and it would take hours to untie the tongues and put them somewhere. He is thoughtless. The way he treats Slob Child. Thoughtless. But she had a mask. Those masks could be dangerous. They might not come off. Well, it would be less to clean up.

"They wouldn't listen to him. He kept asking them where he was supposed to sleep. 'Where am I supposed to sleep, Officer?' He must have said it six times and they just wouldn't even look at him."

You're not supposed to sleep. We're never going to sleep again. We have to stay awake and have a meeting. We have to decide: Are we going to barricade or not? What does it mean to barricade? To barricade means to make free territory, to barricade is liberation. What does it mean not to barricade? Not to barricade is protest. Protest means implicit recognition of their legitimacy. Now, do we have to say it all over again? How many times?

"They are so arrogant. They wouldn't answer his question. Where *was* he supposed to sleep?"

The dawn grew brighter.

·

"Then one of the cops turned around and hit that boy with the point of his club, jammed it as hard as he could into his stomach. Another cop hit him on the head. The boy fell on the pizza, face first. I never saw anything like it, Ellie, did you hear, I never saw anything like it."

Ellie faced her roommate in the grey light. She looked at the girl, not knowing how long. The pipe had gone out. The roommate lit it while Ellie puffed it back into life. Sleep, she remembered reading, evacuated the brain, carried off the trash, useless memory of trivia and emotion that piled up and clogged the pipes during the day. So, she reasoned, if she went to sleep she would forget something, but what, which, how could sleep know what was trash and what was important in all that the day had stored into her tired brain cells?

"That's awful. Policemen shouldn't do that," Ellie said. It sounded lame. Roger or Shapiro would have a better rejoinder about the pigs, the system, tactics which would have made her roommate into a revolutionary, but Ellie decided she didn't believe all of that political stuff. "Did they hurt him badly?" she asked the roommate, and then lost the answer in a slow involvement in herself. The slow coming up and embracing of clouds through an airplane window. Slow sadness for the boy, spreading out, like vapor in the sky—a widening, generalized, unfixed sadness, and how interesting to feel sad and watch it, sad girl with pipe, smoking for unhappy people, police people, boy people, radical people, parent people, people people, eating grey stew meat behind the barricades, the Negroes on the trees, tingling against each other, merry noises in the breeze.

"We have to be together and not pay attention to the confusion, I've decided," said Ellie, "and if we do that, we could make something beautiful—something free, not liberated, or political, cutting people up, but free, you know, free-free. Why can't I ever express what I feel? . . . No practice."

"Ellie, you're skulled!"

"The SKULL! 'The morphogenesis of no part of the vertebrate body has been more thoroughly explored and documented than the SKULL! This very wealth of facts makes it difficult to construct an account which is meaningful to the student just being introduced to the history of the SKULL! It is so easy to become submerged in a sea of cranial parts and lose sight of the flow of morphogenetic events giving rise to the SKULL!'"

"You really are, Ellie."

"I could get an A on that test, but I'll never take it."

From the Verbal History Project:

YALDELL: Frankly, I mean talking honestly, I think we were divided, disorganized, and, well, Fletcher Hall was our last chance to continue to run this University. That's just my opinion. I mean, it just got to be a more confused situation with pressures from all sides, and everybody trying to run the place except the people who had the responsibility. And they—well, I'd rather not say what I think some of them were doing.

But you were asking me about what? The day after Fletcher Hall and Philosophy, right? It's hard to keep the time sequence in order. I guess you'll never know all the things that were happening. So much was going on. Nobody was in a position to see or know everything, and then people were tired. That's a very important point. One thing I learned in the Green Berets is get your sleep. Food's optional, but you can't function without sleep. During that period—the night of Fletcher and Philosophy—and right through the next forty-eight hours at a minimum, I doubt that McVey or Hungerford and the rest of them got ten hours of sleep between them. It was a bad situation. They had to work out of Rennecker Hall, very makeshift and trying. They were using Pomfret's and Blackie's offices. I don't know whether their lack of sleep really affected their judgment, but it had to make them snappish and it slowed things up. They weren't sharp. Their reaction time to all the stuff that was happening got longer and longer. It had to have an effect.

Relatively speaking, I was rested. My wife brought me a sleeping bag, and I sacked out on my office floor. I felt that somebody who was closely involved in all this should be reasonably fresh. I didn't get it all at once—I got pulled out of the bag when Philosophy was taken—still, I had at least six hours of sleep, so I was ready for the next day, which was a long one, a long disaster. But I was in a good position to see a lot of it. I probably spent more time with McVey and Hungerford—well, I know I did—that day than any other.

The first thing, I got a call from Blackie. He said McVey and Hungerford wanted to see me to get my assessment of the "morale factor." Morale factor was the big word that morning. I told Blackie it stunk. He said I should come over to Rennecker and repeat that. I did. Hungerford didn't say anything. Sat there like the air had gone out of him, his flaps and creases twitching. McVey asked a lot of questions in that way of his. I must say he kept his composure. Very methodical, concise. What about this? What about that? I finally said, "Look, people are irritated and confused. Apparently there are no rules at this University. Every day they wake up and the chaos is bigger. They're getting angry. They're going to go over to the other side out of pique at the Administration if nothing else. The situation at the gates is aggravating everybody. The police don't know what they're doing. They're letting in people they should keep out, and vice versa." I told him I'd heard a confirmed report, let's call it a rumor, the police had roughed up a couple of undergraduates trying to get on the Square so they could go to their dorms.

I suggested we recruit some faculty to man the gates. The faculty group, which I guess was started by Professor Mirsky, was meeting in Tappan Lounge. I don't think they had a formal name yet, Faculty Emergency Committee or anything like that. I suggested they be asked to control things at the gates. At least they could have seen to it the students as well as the non-student revolutionaries got in. I can't tell you what a mess it was. Hundreds of people at every gate, lined up shouting, confusion, the radicals passing ID's out to their non-student friends.

INTERVIEWER: During this period wasn't the Administration trying to contact the people in the buildings to see if they could be talked out?

YALDELL: We had the two urbanologists from Harvard-MIT who were supposed to be in communication with the black students. As far as I know, nothing much was being done with the whites in Fletcher and Philosophy. I may be wrong about that. You have to remember it was very confusing. People were coming in—I don't know—from everywhere offering to help, to negotiate. Professor Mirsky was in, and other people from the Faculty Emergency Committee. The antis—mostly Greeks and athletes—were running around. My impression from that morning was that the Administration was still concentrating on the blacks. I think they felt if they could get the blacks out of Ripon without trouble, the whites would come out or they could drag them out without having to worry about the ghetto marching in here and burning us down.

We made some miscalculations. There was a serious underestimate of the number of whites involved, and it was also thought that a high percentage of the whites were non-students. It turned out eight-five or ninety per cent *were* students, but nobody knew that then.

INTERVIEWER: Except Nexus.

YALDELL: Yea, I guess so. Except Nexus. We weren't on very good terms with Nexus and not likely to believe them if we had been. And, remember, this was before Gilmore was liberated, to use their word. Gilmore didn't happen until late that afternoon, and Witherspoon and Eliot were that night. The whites weren't taken nearly as seriously as they should have been. But my God! I was as much to blame as anybody for that. They were asking me for my opinion of the morale and general student feeling, and I tell you, I had no idea what was going to happen. Kids did things I still wouldn't believe if I hadn't seen them with my own eyes. I thought I knew these kids. Naturally not all fifteen thousand undergraduates, but enough so I had a feeling, and I believe I did. I swear even now that there is some truth in what I said about people switching and going over to the Bolsheviks because they looked to us for leadership, for direction, and also for some recognition that we were going to do something about the issues. I'm sure I've said this before in this interview—say you really want all of this stuff?—okay, well, as I think, there were issues. The black demands, some of them were completely unreasonable, but not all; a lot weren't, and that's another thing. People didn't want to go against the blacks. There was idealism in this. If Elias and the SDS hadn't used it, well, forget that. I'm convinced now, a lot of kids went into those buildings and stayed there till the end. God! what a nightmare that was! They did it because they felt for the blacks, they really did. They were used, taken, conned, lied to, exploited by Tully Haskins, by B.J., Roger Elias, by Shapiro, but those kids were going to stay in those buildings until the blacks came out. They were going to show the blacks white kids had balls, that America wasn't just racist, not just the Algiers Motel, that there were whites who would be with them to the end of ends, till the fire came, and God! You gotta hand it to 'em, they were.

Which brings up a point. The strategy of going after Ripon Hall did make sense even in the white context. It just didn't work I guess. I don't know. I had nothing to do with that. What I do know is that McVey and Hungerford had a press conference which made things worse. They up and told the world that the University was functioning normally. Well, it wasn't doing anything of the sort, but it's the kind of Papal statement we make around here. Whatever it is, the Pope always says nothing's changed, we're really making out okay down here in the catacombs. There were thousands of students who could see we weren't functioning normally. What does that make us look like to them? Liars or ninnies, and ninnies most likely. Also, that gave students and faculty who live off campus here the assumption that it was business as usual. Maybe we can get along without Fletcher. No classes meeting there, and Ripon is relatively small, but Philosophy isn't, so we had I don't know how many furious teachers and students shut out of their classes, wandering around, gumming things up, and being added to the crowds —or should I say mobs?

The Harvard-MIT urbanologists were crammed into a barricaded alcove just inside of an entrance to Ripon Hall. They exchanged slow words with Tully Haskins as B.J. listened. The black demands had shifted: amnesty was demanded as a pre-condition to negotiations. The urbanologists returned to Rennecker, where Hungerford is reported to have said again that the University would not negotiate. There was a long meeting through the morning to work out a formula around the word negotiate, which the urbanologists would in due course take back to Ripon, where the prevailing opinion was that the time for serious talk had not yet come. The white students had captured two buildings; they might take more. It made sense to wait and let the pressure build: the ghetto, the black community, the Big Black Cats, Mungo—the expectation was they would march on the University. B.J. alone sat with head down against the wall, remembering the white man's violence, floating in the salts of pessimism and gloomy conviction it would end badly.

Nexus, located in the basement of a dorm, was an excited confusion. Here in a storm of meetings, groceries, revolving mimeograph machines, poster paint, and music, the SRAC (Student Revolutionary Action Committee) was beginning life. Here were Roger, Shapiro, The Supreme Cream, and Ellie, answering phones and running errands. Here also came Roysterman and an infinity of other concerned clergy on the hunt for relevance; here came radicals from across town on the hunt for a field of action to test ideas and ideals; here came newsmen, civil liberties lawyers, fagged-out middle-aged joy riders from half a dozen other schools in search of clients, youth, kicks, unknown confrontation on the barricades.

In Tappan Lounge the informal and continuous faculty meeting and kaffeeklatch grew into a serious debate about what to do. Upwards of five hundred teachers were present, mostly liberal and low ranking, but not all. Myron Mirsky and the astronomer were there, as was Anatol Wiegel and some of the University's other famous professors. Eldon Russell in academic gown stayed for several hours but didn't speak, but Brailis Monteferrent (physics), Andreas Volanyi (math), Franz Jacques (English) did. Arthur Wythe, the brilliant young associate professor of history, was in the chair most of the afternoon, and Henry Wilson, the philosopher and most renowned member of the faculty, gave the first, formal-type speech.

"My text for the day comes from an article written by Zbigniew Brzezinski. I brought a few Xeroxes along, but I can see now, not nearly enough. For those who might wish to consult the original, it appeared on page twenty-three of the June 1, 1968, number of *The New Republic*. It's called "Revolution and Counterrevolution (But Not Necessarily about Columbia)." Henry Wilson got a titter on that. Professionally, he'd made his name in more abstruse kinds of new logics, but his manner wasn't obscurantist. A tall, white-haired man who was given something of a gracious air by his blue, double-breasted suit, he was a poised and effective public speaker.

"We're told to make way for the Revolution. Its red flag actually hangs on the roof of Philosophy Hall. With this goes vast amounts of claptrap rhetoric about the wave of the future, historical inevitability. However, every upheaval is not a revolution. Some upheavals are inconsequential spasms, others, as Mr. Brzezinski suggests, are 'counter-revolutions operating in the name of revolutions.' The sign of a counter-revolution is that it has no program or that it seeks to shape the present by understandings of the past. That is what we are faced with now at this University. The people fortifying themselves in our classrooms do have complaints and grievances, valid ones, ones that an administration less inept, less fumbling, less pathetically ineffectual, and less taken up with the obsession that toothpaste can finance a modern university would have done something about long before we got in the mess we're in. But complaints do not a revolution make.

"Who are these people making this fuss? Brzezinski calls them the 'historically obsolete,' and their revolution 'the death rattle of the historical irrelevants,' that is, people who no longer have an important or necessary role in the rational, technical, electronic ways we now run this society. They are our equivalent to the unemployed and uselessly over-educated middle class of the Arab world, perennially rioting and boiling up because they are not needed. The people leading this trouble here are the modern American academic counterpart to the Cairo street mob, the useless, declassed, displaced, demoted and demeaned remainders of the tradition and training we call the humanities; they are as well the dregs of the social sciences, the sentimental, unprofessional, unequipped members of those disciplines who can't make it as scientists.

"Because they can't run the machines, more exactly the computers, they want to break them. And they may. Retrograde, counter-revolutionary movements have won before in history. If they don't succeed in capturing this place, they may destroy it as a social institution, they may even destroy it physically. May I remind you, these non-violent souls are entrenching themselves in the building while the Square is rife with rumors—which I can't say are true or false—that bombs and guns are being smuggled in here.

"We have gotten to a point now where we can't afford any more quixotic, idiosyncratic shenanigans by professors who think they can indulge their whims without taking the rap for it. If you sympathize any more, if you empathize, if you pacify, appease, placate any more, you won't have a University. This thing is growing worse by the hour."

Mirsky and the astronomer looked at each other and imperceptibly shook their heads. Younger faculty were on their feet demanding recognition from Arthur Wythe. "I have not finished, Mr. Chairman," said Henry Wilson.

"Logicians are insane," Mirsky whispered to his friend. "They can't distinguish between reason and wisdom. Henry Wilson is going to go his consistent way, from proposition to proposition, all the way to the madhouse dragging us with him."

Wilson was continuing: "A week ago twenty policemen could have ended the mess here. Today two hundred are needed simply to guard the gates, and what it will take to evict these people from the buildings, I can't guess, but—"

Twenty or thirty men were up on their feet, shouting and

interrupting the philosopher. "No police! No cops!"

"Well, you're going to have to use police or surrender this school," Wilson replied. Boos and more cries of no police.

"I don't welcome the police on a university campus," Wilson said, "but you must understand that three buildings have been taken already. The moral cowardice of the people charged with the duty of running this school is going to incite more and more of the moderate majority to go over to the other side, and there'll be other buildings. I promise you—"

"Point of information," a voice in the back of the room cried out, and when it was recognized said, "Well, I really rise to give information, but it's germane. Gilmore Hall has just been taken."

Henry Wilson put on an I-told-you-so expression while the room went alive with talk. An infuriated young biologist got to his feet shouting, "Objection! Objection!"

"I don't think that's a motion in parliamentary procedure," Arthur Wythe responded.

"If it isn't, it ought to be," the biologist said. "I object to Administration stooges coming in here and staging this charade. If Mr. Wilson wants to hold a Hungerford-McVey pep rally he ought to get his own hall, and let those members of the faculty who don't think this is the 'death rattle of the historical irrelevants' get on with trying to save this university and our students. Those are our students in those buildings, not 'historically obsolete' pieces of machinery."

Sustained applause. One hand on hip, the other resting on the back of the chair in front of him, Henry Wilson waited it out.

"I'm not going to reply in kind to those words and turn this meeting into a brawl," he said, and there was applause for him. "Ideally," Wilson resumed, "if Mr. Brzezinski's correct—I hope you all take the time to read his article—

ideally, we should be reformers moving in now to undercut and isolate the radical leadership by taking care of just and reasonable grievances, then, to use Brzezinski's words, 'If the leadership cannot be physically liquidated, it can at least be expelled . . .' You'll have to excuse the *realpolitik* word 'liquidated,' but as a State Department consultant and a professor at Columbia, I suspect Mr. Brzezinski has learned through experience that you don't kid around with something like this."

"This is just awful!" It was the biologist on his feet again. "I can't believe I'm hearing right. A professor at this University using the most brutal expressions of totalitarianism in connection with our students! Mr. Chairman, would you ask Mr. Wilson to come to the point and give us his final solution?"

"I am almost finished," Wilson said, mild exasperation in his voice. "This *must* be said and listened to with open minds. In these situations, intellectuals typically play a tragic, foolish part. Being intellectuals they see both sides and therefore appoint themselves as mediators, but in the end they are used by the insurrectionists because they are politically inept and they exaggerate their power. What I am asking you to understand is that if we do that here we're going to make this mess worse. We can't afford to. We're running out of time and options. We have to choose sides, and the only side we can take is the Administration's. I'm not asking you to take it blindly. Martin Hungerford is an incompetent, blubbering, money-raising fuddy-duddy. He should be gotten out of here, but not now. Today we must back him, and once this thing is put down, we can exact Hungerford's head from the Board of Trustees."

"Myron," the astronomer leaned over and asked, "does Henry Wilson want to be president of this University? Is that it?"

"We're all acting abnormally," Mirsky replied.

Wilson wasn't finished speaking, but someone else had dashed into the back of the room and was shouting, "Confrontation! There's a very serious confrontation in front of Fletcher going on right now. Between the radicals and the conservatives. We need faculty to break it up."

The biologist was on his feet complaining again: "I object to this! We can't have an orderly meeting if we're going to be constantly interrupted by these theatrical announcements." As he spoke, fifteen or twenty faculty, affixing white armbands to their coat sleeves to indicate either their neutrality or their status, prepared to go out and act as peacemakers. "I think we should act as a body," the biologist continued. "I don't think we should go running out there as individuals. I'd also like to point out that it will be a useless dissipation of our strength to play neutral pacifier in this situation. We are simply being used by the Administration. Let's get on with this meeting. If we all vote to put on white armbands and assume this role, I'll go along with it, but I think it should be debated."

He sat down and Henry Wilson got up again. "I agree with the speaker. Spending our time breaking up fist fights between the students is a waste of our prestige, which should be saved so it can be thrown in on the side of the Administration decisively. It will also prolong this crisis, and the longer it lasts, the more unthinking converts will be made, not so much deliberately by the radicals but by the whole deceiving, falsely liberating, pseudo-exhilaration of the experience. This thing must be stopped; it must be put down now."

The debate stretched out into an inconclusive supper recess. On the Square the broiling irritation of faction rasping against faction grew in anger. The seizure of Gilmore all but stopped the operations of the University's liberal arts division. Too many teachers and students were now locked out of their classrooms to regroup and carry on. The outlying technical schools functioned normally, their halls so quiet you could hear the hands on the wall clocks change position. In engineering (all branches from electrical to automotive), in the schools of library science, social work, business administration, education, international relations, and the specialized centers, law and medicine, the rebellion had not penetrated. The last two, law and medicine, were showing some weak spots, but basically the career people who came to the university to get certified for a job, moved along untouched.

From the Verbal History Project:

MC VEY: We were terribly aware that time was running out. Those who say we failed to show initiative during this period are wrong. President Hungerford and I went without sleep, literally without sleep, for several days. Working around the clock. We did everything that could be done, but it's clear now that Nexus leaders never intended to reach an agreement. They were not working in good faith. They wanted to add to the radical martyrology; they wanted polarization; they wanted the students to experience disillusionment with our political and decision-making processes.

We did everything to find an agreement. We had the urbanologists working with the black students in Ripon Hall; we worked with the representatives of the Faculty Emergency Committee, that is, Professors Mirsky, Wythe, and Volanyi, but Nexus laid down a general and complete amnesty as a pre-condition for meaningful discussions. That was out of the question. It may be the leaders of Nexus—some people have said this—didn't realize how late the hour was getting and how few options were open, but we were confronted with an impossible situation. Democracy is basically procedural; they were attempting a *putsch*. And there were pressures—I should rather call it an intense concern—from other places. The trustees. Other universities. The society at large, which has a great and I think necessary vested interest in an institution like ours. We were running out of time. We had hoped to close off the campus and communicate only with our students, but a large number of non-student radicals from the outside continued to get in anyway. This has been poo-poohed, but the Police Counter-Intelligence Unit identified these people. They were, again, literally bomb-throwers, narcotics users, and they were bringing in firearms. We were aware of the enormous faculty sentiment against the use of the police. Unfortunately, these same faculty have never said what a school is supposed to do when part of it is physically seized by armed individuals from the outside. . . . Yes, it is true we increasingly had to rely on the police. Our small campus security group was never designed with the thought it would be called upon to deal with something like this. Throughout we strove to suppress what could be called an armed rebellion, while preserving traditional liberty. I realize that an expression like "armed rebellion" is startling, but no one can understand what we faced and therefore why we did what we did until he accepts the fact that we had an armed rebellion here, planned and fomented by non-university forces that have done the same thing elsewhere. The only difference between what has happened here and at Berkeley or Columbia or San Francisco State is that we are another rung higher up in the escalation.

INTERVIEWER: Had you decided to have a special convocation of the faculty and student body and then called it off?

MC VEY: There was some discussion about having a special convocation, but it was ruled out for security reasons. Chief Manfried felt it would be virtually impossible to prevent non-students from sneaking in.

Nexus was making Ellie mildly sick. Too much of the

wrong things were happening. Whole echelons of revolutionary bureaucrats had formed themselves out of air and were organizing everything in an officious, self-importantly didactic way. When they wanted something done, instead of just asking, they made speeches explaining why they wanted it done, what theory was behind it, and in what way it differed from the way a bourgeois would have solved the problem. And at the very end they would all repeat that they were telling her this because she could not participate unless she understood; they wanted no drones in the movement.

Two more buildings were going to be taken that evening, and there was a lot of intense, hushed-up talk which depressed Ellie. She didn't like the mood created by people running in and grabbing other people to take them off and tell secrets. The way it had happened at Gilmore had pleased Ellie. No plan or foreknowledge. All day long the students in more and more classrooms had debated the whole question and decided not to leave. After the place had been taken they informed Nexus. Ellie had wanted to go over to Gilmore for hours; she thought she probably wanted to stay there and not see Nexus again. Let whatever Nexus does in our name be done without our knowledge.

Around ten in the evening Professor Mirsky had come with two other faculty members and met with Shapiro and Roger and a couple of the others for a long time. After they left the two had had a worse than usual fight. Shapiro had accused Roger of lying to Mirsky.

"I didn't lie."

"Well, it was the same thing as lying. You made them believe we'd take something less than amnesty or we'd settle for whatever terms the blacks settle for. The committee didn't tell you to say that."

"What the hell difference does it make, Shapiro?"

"It makes a lot of difference. How the hell can we negotiate if they don't know what we want. I mean, Roger, it's just irresponsible to play games like that."

"Tactics, asshole. Tactics."

"Don't call me names. Answer. Why did you lie to them?"

"They're going to go over to Rennecker Hall and tell McVey and Hungerford that we'll settle for a compromise, a formula on amnesty, and then Hungerford won't give at all, and they'll report back to the faculty that the Administration is being completely unreasonable."

"Roger, you're a child. A dangerous child."

Then the name-calling began. Ellie couldn't take it and slipped out of the room, through the corridors of people painting signs, lugging groceries, turning press releases on the mimeograph machine, arguing, standing, singing. Outside the building, Mirsky and the two other teachers were talking, discussing whether they should go immediately to Rennecker or first report to Tappan Lounge where the faculty was meeting around the clock.

"As I understand it, labor mediators never divulge any change in the different sides' positions on the theory that making it public also makes it more difficult for people to change their position," Wythe was saying.

"But, Arthur," Mirsky replied, "we're not labor negotiators. We're faculty representatives charged with finding out what Nexus wants and reporting back. We haven't been given a mandate to act as go-betweens without consulting the body."

Ellie could listen to them without their seeming to notice her, but they made her woozy, too. They were like Shapiro and Roger, never getting to the point. What was the point? Hard to say, but not Nexus, not negotiations, take a point, lose a point, amnesty, your side, my side. Sil would know, but he wasn't around. The Supreme Cream would know; it would be evident by the smile on his face and the sequences of private, personal humiliations in his eyes, but he never knew how to say. The Supreme Cream always had to be intuited, and Ellie wasn't sure that would be enough for her despondent mood.

"Well, all right, Myron," Arthur Wythe was saying, "let's report to the body that there appears to be some slack in the Nexus position, let's not call it movement, just slack, and come in with a recommendation that we feel out the Administration."

"Sounds sensible," Mirsky responded.

Sensible? It was crazy. Ellie underwent something like an impulse to walk the few steps over to them and say it. It's crazy. Slack in the position, is it? Let's not call it a movement. It darn well better be a movement of people. Not to be felt out with a recommendation. Slack in the body. You men are slack in the body. Where was the girl who was giving that speech about women being niggers? She was out in front of Rennecker Hall the night of the car, the night of The Supermarket Is a Boon to Mankind. Well, they say niggers have soul. Better a soulful nigger than talking in the night about slack in the position, feeling out the Nexus like a man. Ellie left them, walking through the Square in the general direction of the Mother of Knowledge where a large group of antis were together in loud misery and temper.

There were girls with them. Many of them were surrounding Eldon Russell. Two or three of the boys Ellie recognized. She'd dated them, knew their type, sympathized with their lamentations. She moved closer to hear what Russell was saying and realized he was drunk and unhinged, talking about youth and ideals and wiping wet, sniffling features with a corner of his academic gown, telling them he couldn't help them, telling them he was praying they'd find the strength to help themselves, telling them he thanked God he was too old to live long enough to see what was in store for them. They stood around him in serious, square-shouldered neatness, their ties in place and their hair combed, young men of power who misbehaved only with beer for pleasure, solid young men like their fathers, kind in their way, doing for their families, fishing with their boys, not too far, not too deep, not too much, there to come home to, making homes, being at home, listing their complaints to the origins of Western civilization. Assault from without? Rot from within? The origins of Western civilization fumbled in the suitcase of aphorisms, parallels, warning guidelines, and precedents from the past. Oh, the sad, bad times and the funky morals, no saying applied; the lesson of history was clear, there is none. Save yourselves, cast about, each man for himself, the lumberman is loose in the groves of academe.

Ellie got inside a window at Gilmore, the single unbarricaded portal, immediately before the antis attacked. She was just inside when their ramming reverberations against the front door assaulted the closed air inside the building. She was still listening, deciphering the noise's meaning when the head and shoulders of an anti filled the space in the window. Before the revolutionary guards could repel it and block the window, Ellie looked at the face, read it and recognized it in the dark, and said, "Harvey!"

"Ellie!" the face responded, its attached body unmoving. Behind it another figure climbed on the outside window ledge. It was Mirsky's. The faculty was trying to interpose itself between the combatants.

"Go away, Harvey," Ellie said. She said it so as to convey that this wasn't for him, that he was misplaced, a boy in a room where girls were doing their hair.

"Young man," Mirsky's voice said to the figure named Harvey's rear end, "think a minute. Think a minute before you go any farther."

The figure stayed as it was.

"Harvey, this doesn't concern you. Just go away, Harvey. It doesn't really matter to you. Don't ruin it for other people," Ellie said, and the revolutionary guards waited the outcome before attacking the figure, which continued stiff in the window.

"If you go in there, the others, your associates'll follow, there'll be a fight and people will get hurt. Do you want that on your conscience? Ten, twenty years from now, do you want to have to remember what you caused?" Mirsky asked.

"Please don't talk to me. I don't want to hear—words," the figure in the window said in a labored voice, and rigidified again.

"Look, I know how you feel," Mirsky pursued him. "It's your school, too, and nobody's sticking up for you. You paid your tuition, now you can't get into class and they have communist flags in the windows. But if you care about yourself or the University, you'll be reasonable."

Ellie, addressing the face of Harvey, said, "It'll all be over in a few days, Harvey. It'll go back to being the way it was, so let the people who're involved with it work it out. You don't care. It doesn't matter to you. You're just doing this because you feel left out, and you feel left out because it has nothing to do with you."

The boy in the window lost his rigidity; the tension in his form slacked. "Why did you have to talk to me? I didn't want to hear anything. I asked you not to talk. I didn't want to be reasonable. Why did you?" he asked.

Mirsky answered, "Because I didn't want you to be like those in there. They don't listen. They don't care if somebody's hurt. Come, climb down from the window. You've done a good thing."

"Ellie," the boy ventured as he began backing out, "are you going to stay?"

"I'm going to stay."

"You're not one of them. God, Ellie, you don't believe in their crap."

"I'm involved."

"Oh, hell!" he said, disappearing out the frame of the window back down to the earth, where he stood with Mirsky who talked to him and walked him away.

From the Verbal History Project:

YALDELL: I was there in the room, in the room with them, lots of the time, and *I* don't know what was happening with Hungerford and McVey. They just wouldn't do anything but repeat themselves. Pomfret was useless. He was frigid, uncommunicative—in a stoic despair, sucking on his pipe and saying, if anybody asked, it was a disaster, which everybody knew, but it wasn't over and it was getting worse. Blackie was furious, but keeping it to himself. He never admitted it, but I think he was behind Henry Wilson and the "conservative" petition which showed up around that time asking that appropriate force be used to get them the hell out of those buildings. Of course, it didn't mean anything. We were getting petitions, it seemed to me, like one an hour. You went out on the Square, and if they weren't having a pier nine brawl there were little tables all over with people at them collecting petitions or selling buttons, everything. STOP SDS, End Racism, Close the University, Open the University, buttons, speeches, rallies, fist fights. It was pure chaos.

Which is what you'd expect. No leadership. We simply weren't doing anything. The Mayor's office was whimpering on the telephone that it didn't want to dislodge the blacks from Ripon Hall because of the ghetto, and everybody felt you couldn't go after the white buildings and leave the blacks alone. So we waited for the urbanologists. They'd go and they'd come, and would we see our way clear to guaranteeing this to the blacks or that to the blacks. Hungerford and McVey would get off in another room and talk alone and come back and say yes, and nothing would happen.

Two or three times the urbanologists said they were getting close to an agreement, that it was very, very near. Well, that stopped everything, and then they'd come back and say no, and once they came back and said negotiations had broken off completely, and then they were back on again.

It was Bah-Bah land. Here was this building, blank, black building, which used to be called Ripon Hall, and in there somewhere were those blank, black persons, whose names we didn't know, whom we knew nothing about. Just over there on one side of the Square. Talk about black and white America, non-communication, we were living it. It just got to be insane. As if whatever or whoever was over in that building was magical. All we knew was that there was a guy named Tully and a guy named B.J. Maybe the urbanologists knew more, but they didn't tell us.

I remember there was a lot of talk about "regaining the initiative" and rallying the silent majority. And the phone rang a lot. Did it. And people coming in with plans, suggestions, and contacts into the enemy camp. A swarm of sort of free-lance, diplomatic, entrepreneurial helter-skeltering. I guess they meant well, but most of the day it was the talk about regaining the initiative and the silent majority. Bah-Bah land. I was out on the campus and I'd say it was coalescing, polarizing, there were fewer and fewer uncommitted people, and those that were uncommitted—maybe they were a majority—were totally uncommitted, people who weren't going to support anybody but would just wait and see what happened. I suppose you could think of them as "the quiet, serious student," that's the kind of language that was being used about them, but it was obvious to Blackie and me that they were useless in a fight. We were in a fight.

They couldn't make up their minds. Who couldn't? The people in Rennecker Hall, Hungerford and McVey. Should they close the school? Blackie would hint the truth to them that the University was being closed by other people and disintegrating. We didn't control enough classrooms to open it. I wished the two of them had gone out of the building and walked around the Square, but that was just a sample of it. They couldn't. Martin Hungerford, I don't believe, not at that point, could have walked around his campus, his University which wasn't his anymore. He would have needed a bodyguard. Somebody would have plunked, the radicals or the conservatives, because he was such an ass. But I do have some respect for him. He wanted to fight for his own. It was McVey who was the most indecisive, so calm, analytical, asking questions, getting it straight in his mind, and then starting all over again being calm and asking questions.

Hungerford wanted to have the extraordinary convocation. He wanted to assemble the entire University in the football stadium. Talk to them. I didn't understand what he thought he'd accomplish. Nothing maybe. You know, I have a hunch now—I don't know what I thought then—that he knew it was over, him and the University, and he wanted to go out looking good. He said, he said it more than once, "I don't want to be like Grayson Kirk," meaning that Kirk at Columbia had never faced the student body and had hidden away during the time of the revolution there. But Martin Hungerford believed he was right. He believed in himself. God, like the Bourbons. A little Bourbon king, that's what he was. I do believe what he suffered from more than anything else was that he couldn't measure up to what he thought he should be. He was gutty, you've got to give that to him. I never thought much of him. I mean, he was a blunderer, never knew what was going on, but he had a sense of himself. Ridiculous. Pathetic. He'd sit there collapsed, quiet, probably dead from lack of sleep, and then you could almost see him make the effort, blow himself up and hold the pose till the air went out of him again.

McVey was different, holding on to the little pieces, worrying about stray legalisms, cautious, gave you the idea he knew what he was doing, methodical, but he never did anything. He was against the convocation idea. He kept reminding Hungerford of what happened at Berkeley in the Greek Theater when Kerr faced the students and Mario Savio tried to get to the microphone and campus security stopped him and dragged him off stage. I think the real reason McVey was against the convocation was the fear that Hungerford would get up in front of the thousands and botch it, which he probably would have. Hungerford may have sensed what McVey was thinking, because I remember him saying something touching. You had to feel sorry for him. "I know what I look like. I am a short, stout, little grey man. It's as apparent to me as it is to everybody else that I lack charisma. But I'm the president of the University." He said it to McVey while they were wasting hours trying to decide about the convocation. That's the way he talks, moving from one still pose to another, and nothing in between his little declamations. They say the office can make the man. With Hungerford, the more I saw of him the more the thought came to me the office kept him in existence. Now he's gone and you hear his name, that he's doing this or that, but I don't believe it. I think when he left the presidency he went into non-existence; the job and the personality had fused. I don't see what mode of life was possible for him without the job.

McVey was a different kind of case. Listening, talking, making decisions, doing business, slow but never stopping. I really admired him. Only much, much later I decided he had gone nuttier than anybody else. Hungerford was like a man who knew it was over and what he had to do was die an edifying death. Blackie was the realist, but McVey went on having meetings and planning and getting advice and doing business when there wasn't any business to do. Worrying whether the University should be closed the next day. It was closed. It had been closed on him by the enemy. He was worrying about exams; he was worrying should we extend the semester to make up for lost time. Amnesty, rule XXVII, when does non-violence become force, the proper way to present demands, procedure—and by then it was so simple. Roger Elias was going to burn the school down around our ears or we had to obliterate him.

I got more sleep than anybody else and *my* time sense for this period is disoriented, so maybe it was that night or maybe it was some other time, I do remember Henry Wilson talking to McVey, and McVey saying very calmly to Wilson, who was demanding the cops, the militia, the army, and McVey was shaking no, no, and saying, "You don't use nuclear weapons in a counter-insurgency situation." Toward the end we used military talk a lot. Wilson didn't, I don't think, but he wasn't in the command post much. He was arguing that our friendlies were being intimidated and co-erced over to the other side, but mostly that there was a kind of conversion experience going on, people being taken up emotionally just by what was happening, regardless of what it meant politically. McVey couldn't see it. He wanted meetings, procedures, counter-forces, infrastructures—we were all talking that way—he couldn't see we'd run out of options. The hearts and minds of the student body were being lost out of weakness, out of our refusal to use our equivalent to a nuclear warhead. As I said, it's hard to reconstruct the order things happened in. I do know, though, we were all in the Rennecker Hall command dugout or command post or whatever you want to call it when the un-friendlies escalated. The bomb went off.

It destroyed the corner of the University gym building where the ROTC was located. Throughout the campus there was a quiet, inquiring pause. Then at Nexus the young men looked past each other's faces, recalling the sound of the blast until one of them said, "Somebody's taking care of business," and Shapiro looked down on the table at the yet-to-be-mimeographed manifestos for the coming morning and tried to figure out what it was. At Tappan Hall there were at least five men on their feet, saying, "I don't think it would be wise for all of us to run out. We may be needed as a body. Mr. Chairman, I strongly move we send a small committee to ascertain what has happened and report back."

On the campus were invisible running feet. Shadows, silvered and dark, panting and leaping over hedges, running on lawns, out of breath, urging each other on, hundreds of shapes running through the blackened colors of the night, silent crowds in straining motion toward the gym where there was smoke, firemen, and investigating officials, away toward Manion Gate where police, in heavy columns, were debouching onto the Square and standing in squads. From off somewhere in the dead space between two old classroom buildings rose a trilling uvular, a high warbling note, sustaining its pitch, coming nearer, backing off, promising to whoop down and drop an octave, but not doing so, the cry carried on the air of the night impregnating it with the threat of ambush and surprise.

From other directions came marching antis in sport coats, chanting, "We want police brutality! We want police brutality!" They stood arms folded, the back seams of their coats stretched tight, slacks and bermudas, legs apart, waiting for the policemen to perform their friendly offices. And again, off, away, elsewhere in the dark the cycling dip of keening sound, the cry of Algerians, Viet Cong, Cubans, Guatemalans, Philippinos, calling for sabotage, hit and run, calling out the guerrilla. The noise and the running made a circling swoop of high-frequency energy, moving and growing through the campus, pulling people out of buildings and adding to the current of motion.

Ellie was drawn out of Gilmore. Running, high on her toes, like the TV advertising girls leaping slow motion through surf and beach, feeling like they look, weightless, ordinary motion turned to dance by the trickery of time, she went on with them wondering how her picture of herself could run slower and slower as she ran faster. She tried to accelerate, thinking the picture would stop and she would terminate into the oscillating frequencies of the channel of sound. The thought impeded and broke the process. The picture speeded up, her running slowed down, until the two synchronized and she felt her lungs scraping for air, but she ran on, scared to drop back and be left behind.

Out of the pattern, like unpredictable particles on a photosensitive plate, were the seminarians, medical students, nurses and doctors. They did zigzags in their white coats, red cross arm bands, walkie-talkies, and first-aid equipment. Roysterman was there with them in his clerical collar, enduring the strains and exertions of mind and emotion which affirmed his theology. He and his group set up aid stations, introduced themselves to the police as neutral humanitarians. There was an insane, legalistic officiousness about them as they flew about setting up the rules of war.

The lights in the buildings began to flicker. Phone service went out. In the building where Nexus was located students were running through the hall, yelling, "It's the bust! The bust! Cops are marching on campus. Thirty paddy wagons at the Manion Gate." The mimeograph machine stopped. Boys took their girl friends' hands and leading them out the doors maneuvered through the Square to get to the buildings. They were like people who'd long since made out their wills. People who'd rehearsed their dying and knew what to do, except in the committee room where the perpetual revolutionary meeting was always in session.

Shapiro had gotten up from the table. "It's not the bust," Roger said to him. "Sit down, we've got work to do."

"Cops are massing, Roger. It's over. They're going to attack any minute," Shapiro said, undergoing a fatigued irritation at always having to be the practical, older man. "It's over. They're going to attack. It's going to be like every place else. We're going to be slaughtered, and the ones that aren't slaughtered are going to be arrested, and in three hours the movement'll be over here and that's the end of it. I'm going out and get slaughtered."

"Sit down, scratch your head and listen, will ya, Shapiro?" Roger persisted in a tone of artificial impatience. For once the usual anger was missing, and this made Shapiro stop and wait to hear more. "There isn't going to be a bust. I've been right so far. I'm telling you *I* know these people and there isn't going to be a bust tonight. Bluff. Those cops'll be off campus and back on the avenue in an hour. And if I'm wrong you can't get busted anyway, Shapiro."

"Well, I'm going to be."

"You can't. You're a leader. You're no good in jail. I know you, Shapiro. You're aching to get busted. Preferably you'd like to get your head split open *and* busted to take the guilt away, so you can tell yourself you got what they all got out there. Try and remember you're not guilty of anything. Try and remember the guilty ones are the people who called the cops, the people who run this spaghetti factory, the members of the Board of Trustees, the newspapers, the sweating, indecisive, liberal whores who run this mind-mangling machine. You're not guilty, so sit down."

Shapiro didn't have the energy to argue, so he walked out to look at what was going on. He was on the wrong side of the campus to see McVey, McTavish, and Yaldell hurrying out of Rennecker toward Tappan Lounge. They walked unnoticed in the darkness through a slice of the Square that was reasonably quiet. From the look of them, three quick-

walking men, they could have been inured to the furor of the
bad night. They weren't.

From the Verbal History Project:

YALDELL: It was hairy. I've been in combat, so I know
when to be scared, and I was scared. By this time there were
God knows how many people running around. Jesus, they
were making that weirdo, howling whine and they were
breaking windows. You could hear the tinkle every so often.
And then the cops. They had to be nervous. I'm sure they'd
never seen anything like this, so you had five or six hundred
armed men who were nervous. Well, that's frightening. I
don't care how well trained they are. It was a terrible scene
and those young bitches—pardon me—our students, a whole
bunch of coeds—there must have been a lot of them because
you could hear them chanting distinctly from so far away,
a filthy obbligato: "COPS EAT SHIT! COPS SUCK. FUCK THE
COPS." You could hear them all over the campus. I thought
I knew these kids. Hell, I'm young enough to be part of their
generation, I thought. During that walk over from Rennecker
I resigned from my generation and joined up with dad's. If
that's the wave of the future, I'm baffled, certainly. Mostly
I wish I was born thirty years earlier, because I don't want
to be around when that crowd takes over. Funny, I remember
I was resigning from my generation and McTavish was saying
that he was resigning from being a liberal. "Tonight I found
out I'm a conservative," I remember him saying.

On the way over we ran into Pomfret. He must have just
resigned from something. It was the only time during that
walk that McVey spoke. He saw Pomfret first, standing in
front of a tree, his pipe in his mouth, tears in his eyes. I
mean, the man was stunned. McVey was—you know McVey
has his extraordinary side—he was gentle to Pomfret. Very
kind. Maybe he was touched. I would say he put his arm

around the old guy—although he didn't because that's just not McVey—but he said something like, "Come on with us, old fellow." Naturally not that, but you know, affectionate. But Pomfret was out of it. He couldn't do anything but quote William Butler Yeats. Amazing. I supposed that Pomfret hadn't memorized anything in the last fifty years but the University's football scores: Things fall apart; the centre cannot hold / Mere anarchy is loosed upon the world, / The blood-dimmed tide is loosed, and everywhere / The ceremony of innocence is drowned; / The best lack all conviction, while the worst / Are full of passionate intensity.

That poem. Everybody was quoting it. Literally, I must have had it quoted to me twenty times. And I thought people didn't read poetry any more. I guess Pomfret's center didn't hold. He was useless the whole time as far as I can see. He's a fine man, but he short-circuited out when it finally got through to him this wasn't a fraternity hazing, and McVey must have known it, because he stopped and he really seemed concerned for the old guy. And he was an old guy, suddenly he was emeritus. Blackie had taken over in all but name. That's not much of a statement, because it was chaos and bad planning. Like the bust. They'd had all day to prepare it, make sure the thing was orderly or at least so there wouldn't be lots of accusations. Instead, until the bomb went off, they'd never really thought what bringing the cops on campus would involve. I was in the room. They'd gotten word that half their gymnasium had been blown to kingdom come, and you could actually see Hungerford seize on himself, shake himself, snap into being *the* president of *the* University, one of the ten great institutions of higher learning in the Western world. "I am calling the police now," that's what he said. McVey looked at him and made a nod. *The* president was giving a presidential order. McVey's got gentle blue eyes and they looked at Hungerford. He was unhappy, but hell, they only made a firm, irrevocable, certain, sure, positive, unchangeable decision in order to switch to something else five minutes later.

God, when I think how much they knew about every incident on every campus—don't believe forewarned is forearmed. Everything was laid out. The whole plot. Nothing happened here that didn't happen anywhere else, and still it happened. Like Columbia, like Berkeley, like San Francisco State, and the scenario was the same here. They wanted a bloody confrontation involving as many of the students and the faculty as possible, and so it happened. We played it out like the Easter Story. There was not one moment of real suspense. You knew what was going to happen. For the first time I got some inkling of how come when Martin Luther King would lead those marches down South, looking to get beaten over the head by an atrocity, there was always a sheriff who'd oblige, no matter how much he knew better. It's got nothing to do with contradiction of the system or their tactics or our tactics. You can't be rational with your family, with your relatives, your children. Even when you're mad at them, they're not the enemy. Your tactics, your promises to yourself, your cool head, it doesn't happen that way if you're having a fight with your son or your father. Emotionally we never accepted them as a true enemy, so the decisions were reactions, fits, spurts, splurges.

Everybody's heard what happened in Tappan Hall Lounge. I don't have anything special to add. There were hundreds of faculty there. Don't ask me who. McVey just walked in and asked for the floor and announced it. The calm voice, quite in possession of himself, but not hard. I'd like to remind you that before this started, A. A. McVey was a very popular man here. People had tremendous respect for him, and I still do. Well, I do and I don't. So he was the same McVey he'd always been, calm, polite, not just rational, attentive, a sensitive man, and they knew that and they wanted to hear him. He didn't handle it well, but he was tired. Twenty-four, thirty-six hours no sleep, so he was abrupt, abrupt for him. "I'm afraid I have an announcement to make which many here may disagree with, but the gym has just been bombed, there are five (or was it six) buildings occupied and a mob running amuck through the Square. As a consequence President Hungerford has called the police to restore order. They are assembling on campus now." That ultra reasonable way he talks. I don't have the exact wording, but I know the last thing he said was the cops were already here. The reaction was terrible. People on their chairs shouting, "I resign! Shame! Fascist!" I don't know what McVey thought. He left the room almost immediately. I was supposed to stay and take a sounding before reporting back to Rennecker where McVey returned, so I really got a taste of it. I mean, it was obvious McVey was finished here, too.

INTERVIEWER: I have the chronology, Dr. McVey, but no sense of what happened.

MCVEY: You mean anecdotal material?

INTERVIEWER: Something to make it more than bones.

MCVEY: I don't want to get into personalities. Many of the faculty were upset, seriously upset by the announcement the police had been summoned. It wasn't an easy decision to make for President Hungerford, but he made it and I agreed with him. I think experience elsewhere has shown that simple recourse to force doesn't always work, but you're familiar with what we were faced with. There seemed to be nothing else to do. It was out of hand.

INTERVIEWER: And yet you changed your mind. You pulled the police back. Why?

MCVEY: Just for the reasons that have been given time and time again as this thing has been rehashed. Basically there were two. The vehemence of the faculty protest and the strong doubt, as expressed by Professor Mirsky and some of the others, that it was possible for them to intervene with some effect. The other reason, as I've explained before, was that the police did not have enough men on hand, and there was so much confusion. We had only anticipated clearing the buildings, but wandering crowds of people running around on the Square made this a much larger operation than it had first seemed.

INTERVIEWER: It's been said that you called the police off when you realized they were being brutal or at least using excessive force.

MCVEY: I saw no excessive force used. I'm not saying there was none, but it was a difficult night. The police were outnumbered. This has been gone over a hundred times. These charges arise whenever the police need to be called. We're all aware that the revolutionaries' tactic is to force a confrontation with the police so that they can claim they were brutalized and win public sympathy. Again, I must say it, if it does sound lame: the Administration did not have first recourse to force. The buildings were violently seized, a bomb was detonated, windows were being smashed. I am amazed how in the light of the indisputable facts, some of the aura of the non-violent protest movement manages to cling to these people, despite the facts, despite their own words.

I realize in putting our case this way we run the risk of sounding like dull officialdom droning on. We lack Señor Guevara's panache, but apparently even Fidel Castro found it a little much once the revolution was over and it got to be the day-to-day business of keeping things going.

MIRSKY: Think? I don't know what I thought. It was non-debatable the way he came in, said it, and left. Many people ran out of the room practically with him. The place was in an uproar. I think the ones who ran out went to the buildings to interpose themselves between the students and the police. Well, I wasn't quite ready for that. In fact, I was half-persuaded that there was nothing left to do but use the police. A few more bombs . . . My astronomer friend and I talked for a few minutes and then walked out on the campus to see what was happening. Well, I couldn't believe it. It was madness. The police had no idea what they were doing. They were chasing everybody. Anybody they could get a hold of, pow! the club. The lower middle class in fury. Understandable, but perfectly senseless. The first people I saw them go after were the antis. The boy on the ledge. I had told him after he got off the ledge to go home, but he was there with his buddies shouting, "WE WANT POLICE BRUTALITY!" Well, they got it. I saw a policeman split that poor kid's head open. Terrible. There was a boy who had been non-violent, who had something left in him you could appeal to. The common ground was still there, and they break open his scalp. And the worst was there was no order to it, thousands of kids, hundreds of cops, back and forth, they weren't chasing them off the campus, and each minute it was growing more violent.

A group of us decided to go over to Rennecker Hall and demand to talk to McVey and Hungerford. I don't know how we got there, and when we did we couldn't get in. They had detectives, thugs, arrogant men standing at the door. Authorized personnel, credentials, your name's not on the list, who do you want to see, he's not there—it doesn't take much of that to drive a man radical, at least temporarily, especially when it's your own University, your University. There were eight or ten of us standing in front of the door to Rennecker, full professors, department chairmen, and we could not get in to see the president of our University. We could not. Then these policemen started telling us "clear the area." No "please," nothing, this to Anatol Wiegel. Means nothing. We couldn't "clear the area," because that meant going out in the middle of the Square and getting bopped on the head ourselves. So it ends up that the police run the University. Always the way. Whomever you call to be your protector ultimately becomes your oppressor.

It was immediately after Wiegel had been told to move on by the policeman that a young man from the anthropology department, an instructor or an assistant, came up. He said, "Professor Mirsky?" And, you know, it's remarkable how your civilized habits cling to you, I stuck out my hand. Ridiculous, isn't it? In the middle of a battle, a riot, how do you do, sir, how do you do, shake hands. We shook. But when I took my hand away, I saw and felt it was sticky with blood, and then I realized—the light wasn't too good—the young man had been wounded. It was his blood. When he turned you could see the back of his head was all bloody, on his shirt collar, over his jacket.

I was horrified. I stood there with my hand up looking at it. Wiegel was doing the same. The astronomer, too. All of us. "Go in there and show that blood to McVey and Hungerford," the young man said. I turned around and looked at the policemen and just said, "Open that door!" It may have been the last time in contemporary society that grey hairs will command respect. There must have been something about me that intimidated them. Maybe they were afraid we'd turn out to be big shots. Maybe, maybe, who knows? We got in, found one of those baby-faced third assistant dean of students, told him we wanted medical attention for the young man, and demanded to see Hungerford and McVey.

A minute later McVey was in the hall himself. He was shocked now. And he was. Some of these college administrators where there's been trouble have behaved like brutes. When the innocent are beaten, they just say they shouldn't have been there and they wouldn't have been hurt. That's not McVey. He got a doctor for the young man, personally saw that he was attended to, and then took the rest of us in past all these policemen to see Hungerford.

But a liberal humanist like McVey can't cancel out the feeling I had in Rennecker that night. It disturbed me more than the beating. I had the feeling of the military, the police—which is worse—taking over. Soldiers in my experience may be stupid, and they may practice cruelty in war, but they don't like it. They have a code. I don't put much store on it, honor, tradition, but it sets some limits and provides a ground for shaming them, telling them they haven't lived up to their own standards. Cops have no traditions. They're always the dirty workers and they contaminate everything. Even the baby-faced assistant deans began to take on the looks of security men.

So that's the way it is. We live in the era of the cop, cops spying on cops spying on cops. They talk about their proliferations and explosions, births, garbage, pollution, but nothing has bred faster than cops in the last fifty years. Everywhere around the globe more and more societies have to depend on salaried snoops and brigades of uniformed muscle men for social control. When I was a boy, only Europeans had secret police and political police, now you don't open business before you've got your security component, capability—you know all the words they use. But cops can't bring security; they only bring more cops.

I'm not talking about the rights and wrongs of the different sides. I'm remembering how I felt going down the corridor for the meeting with Hungerford and McVey, realizing how they were being imprisoned by their protectors, looking at all the *gendarmerie* in my University. Eh! What the hell . . . you want to quit. You want to put your palms up and say it doesn't matter, because by then it was already irretrievable, and we were already so tired that the best brains in the world or not, we didn't have a clear idea of what we were doing. We came in and asked Hungerford if he knew what was going on in the Square. I don't know what he answered, except one thing. He said he hadn't been out of his command dugout because the security people told him it was safer for him to stay put. But they were getting reports, maybe even from the police. They must have had some idea they wouldn't be able to rout two thousand people out of those buildings that night when they couldn't even clear the grounds of the bystanders.

They were unprepared. Another case of believing one's own propaganda. It had come to them from on high they were faced with a few score radicals and as many non-students. Even after it was all over, with the hospitals overflowing and jails jammed, they were still issuing statements claiming it wasn't our dear children. But that's later. Then we told the two of them they had to stop the bust immediately, if for no other reason than it wasn't busting the revolution but only innocent heads, which was making more revolutionaries. Actually, by then it was too late. The Sorelians, as I like to call Elias and his gang, had drenched the place in the *sturm und drang* and we professors were playing out an idealistic illusion. There was no academic community left; there were only two sides fighting to make their opponents lose, using outside reinforcements, ideological and military. We professors were preposterous.

Oh, but we thought we'd won a great concession because Hungerford said he'd call off the police. At least I think we thought we'd won a concession. I can't be sure of anything. The catch, though, was that we had to produce. "This is Friday night," he said, and this part I remember because everything that happened subsequently took place under the gun of this deadline, "We mean to have this institution open for business Monday morning. If the faculty can arrange the evacuation of the buildings between now and Sunday night, it would be a wonderful thing. We want peace on this campus and we'll be grateful to whomever brings it about, but if those people are still in the buildings Sunday night, they will be evicted, you can be sure of that, quite."

Quite, quite. A stuffed shirt, but armed and dangerous. They would be grateful to us if we negotiated unconditional surrender on the other side. In the cold light of day, that's what it amounted to. The bloody denouement was to be broken off and postponed for forty-eight hours, when, of course, it would be resumed with a ferocity which marks it as historic. We didn't, we couldn't foresee anything like that then, the actual killing of people. My closest friend on the faculty. I don't believe it yet. No, we thought we'd gotten something out of Hungerford and we'd get some more out of the Administration, but here, we were misled, or we misled ourselves. Hungerford said nothing during the discussion, but he was there when McVey said the Administration's position wasn't fixed, that they'd bargain.

We walked out of there believing we had something. A little light. We decided to go back to Tappan Lounge and tell them, if anybody was there, that we'd gotten the Administration to call off the police. But it was an hour and a half before we actually were able to get there because we were driven off the campus ourselves. The police were still running amuck. The order to break off and retreat hadn't gotten to them yet, so when we got just outside Rennecker Hall, talking among ourselves, they came along, drove us into this terrified mob of people they were chasing back and forth, and finally out Manion Gate. That's where Wiegel broke his arm, out on the street when a policeman on a three-wheeled motorcycle tried to run him down. Well, you've had testimony on that. Just let me get on the record; it was the Chicago Democratic Convention over again. The whole reprise.

And we were the preposterous professors. Can you imagine it? Helter-skelter in the streets with the cops chasing

us. My friend the astronomer and I were helping Wiegel.
God knows where the rest went. So we were the professors,
the third force, the mediators . . . pathetic. Looking back,
I ask myself did I know how ridiculous we were . . . so
powerless? I like to think I did. I like to think that many
of us on the faculty did what we did because this was a rare
struggle in which you'd be ashamed to associate with either
side, no matter who wins. A rationalization? Yes, maybe
it was.

We didn't get back to Tappan Lounge until dawn. The
place looked like a hospital emergency room. The Medical
Committee for Human Rights had cots in there, and they
were treating people. Blood and hysteria. Awful! Obviously
we weren't going to get anything done for a few hours anyhow until things settled a little. We couldn't spare the time
to wait. It was Saturday morning and we had only till
Sunday night, but I went to sleep anyway. I had to sleep.

Ellie was taken out of the crowd by The Supreme Cream.
He picked her out of the screaming, infuriated people in his
acrobatic way, seeming to do easy flips and leaps, guiding
her like a dance partner away from the danger. She was
grateful to him, for she'd seen and felt enough of it, and
he'd come when she was ready to break away. The Supreme
Cream could win over any wall or barrier, float through
police lines; his physical grace made him unconfinable, he
could soar over, slip through, leap past any object made to
retain people; he always seemed to enter rooms on a rope
from a second-story window. He took her in his swift way
off campus to the Slob Child's.

Ellie, enlivened by the excitement, went with him without conversation. She didn't want talk to distract her inven-
tory of the feelings that had come up inside her in response
to the violence she'd seen and the fear she'd felt. A zesty
alertness quickened. The sight, sound, and smell of the

street's night dinge was powerfully strong. Ellie, who lived in misty pastels, was happy in the first full acuity of her senses, taken up, delighted, outside herself.

"Revolution is liberation. Liberation is revolution," she said in explosive exhilaration as she and The Supreme Cream came into Slob Child's place, where the air was close with pot, tobacco, lacquer, and paint.

Several Fuckheads were dozing, sitting on the floor, their heads back against the wall, their eyes open but sightless; another was prone on the floor. Sil was active. Smoking hash and moving around the room, he was perfecting the details of Ignorance. Ignorance was in an unrecognizable condition, a pile of plaster, papier-mâché, and wire parts not yet assembled. That would be done in a little while when Sil would kick the Fuckheads back into contact; they would help him sneak Ignorance part by part back onto campus where her revulsive, double-headed shape would be put together so she would fit exactly over the Minerva, and there in her usurped prominence, slathering Ignorance would hold up her sceptre and shock the dawn.

Sil passed the hash pipe to Ellie and The Supreme Cream. Slob Child, crouching in the kitchen doorway feeding the cats bits of tuna, got none. The pipe had gone out. Sil took it back, sliced off a few more shavings with a razor, put them in the pipe, and ignited the dope. He was watching Ellie as he did. He continued to study her as he inhaled and passed the pipe again. He'd never paused over her before, but something about her had caught his attention. "You're different," he told her. "Yeah, maybe you are liberated . . . No, you're not. I know." He made a little grin of understanding. "Danger makes you horny. It turned you on. People get their heads smashed in, get hurt bad. You don't know, maybe somebody's been killed tonight. Somebody's gonna get killed . . . One person, anyway, you, The Supreme Cream. You're not gonna be alive at the end of this, Cream. You know that, don't you?"

After The Supreme Cream had exhaled the smoke, he replied, saying, "Sorta. I've got that feeling."

"That's a sick thing to say, both of you. It's bad luck. Don't!" said Ellie. She was talking fast. The other two were more relaxed.

"Cream's got bad luck. Slob Child did his horoscope. Bad, bad, bad," said Sil. "He's gonna die. Hey, Slob Child, you got his horoscope still? Where death is in his house, no life in his cusp. I don't understand that shit, but I believe it and I can smell things about people, like I could smell how the fighting an' all that makes you horny."

"That's something you can't control," Ellie told him.

"Does it make you feel bad, people gotta die for you to know that you have a muscle just for making fucking feel good?"

"I'm not making anyone die."

Slob Child said. "The fucking muscle has a name. Pubococcygeus."

"But the dying's what's liberated you," Sil continued. "Revolution is liberation, you said. You're a sort of war profiteer. You're gonna get something out of this, Ellie, if you live. I don't get any feeling about what's going to happen to you."

"You're not being fair, and anyway, what's going to happen to you?" Ellie asked.

"Oh man, I'm gonna go on. So's Slob Child and the cats. Don't forget the cats. If you two screwed, I could sketch you. I did a sketch once of an old woman, a beer lush with almost no hair on her head, just a few gray curls. She was screwing a one-legged man."

"I wouldn't think you'd be interested in us," said Ellie. "Aren't we a little too ordinary, or are we that disgusting, too?"

"Cut it out, Sil," The Supreme Cream said, and looked shy.

"How d'ya know those two were disgusting? Maybe it

was beautiful, what they did with each other. Maybe it felt the same as it would if you two screwed. Maybe it's not bodies but heads that are disgusting. Maybe if I sketched you and the Cream screwing, I might make him into a skeleton and you into a sticky, simple-celled invertebrate that clutches and swallows and gets what she needs everywhere, all the time."

The Supreme Cream groaned and made as if to pick up a section of Ignorance to take it over to the Square.

Sil took up a pencil and paper. "The Cream is a special case," he said, "works out in the gym but doesn't want anybody to see his body. I used to think he's a fag, but he's not. He's just afraid he's a fag, and he's got this beautiful body and he's ashamed he's got it. The Supreme Cream's very mixed up. Not at all together, not homogenized."

"I like to help people," The Cream said.

"Still, you shouldn't die messed up in the head ... Cream, do you think you're smart?" Sil prodded at him.

"Stop it," Ellie said. "Leave him alone. You're only doing this because we won't pose for you."

"Why won't you?"

"Because I want to go back to Gilmore. Revolution *is* liberation. Oh, maybe it isn't, but it's contact with others."

"Commitment?" asked Sil, and he was being sarcastic.

"Possibly," Ellie replied in defiance.

"What's wrong with that, Sil?" The Supreme Cream asked.

Sil looked at both of them for a slow minute as he took the last puff on the pipe, not answering until his eyes had become teary, and then he said, "You don't have to pose for me. I can imagine what I need to know. Let's take Ignorance to the campus."

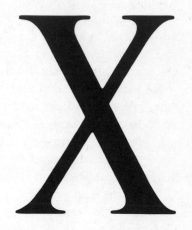

X

YALDELL: Saturday? The thing I remember best about Saturday was the faculty meeting that afternoon. Even though it wasn't a normal class day and most faculty weren't scheduled to be on campus, they started arriving in the late morning with blood in their eyes. What we didn't need at that point was a vote of no confidence or censure even. Blackie saw what their mood was and got several of us on the phone to faculty in the engineering schools and business administration. We told them they just had to turn out and vote against the liberal-arts radicals. We stuffed Oberlin Auditorium. You should have seen me out in front of Manion Gate waving our side on campus and into the meeting.

MIRSKY: Saturday? Saturday was the day of the faculty

meeting in Oberlin Auditorium. You know something? I was so tired, I don't remember how that meeting got started. It was a regular meeting of the Academic Senate. I think it was a result of the indignation, which was very general, against the police. That morning it was an unbelievable scene on campus. Some of the world's most distinguished scholars walking around with bandages on their heads. Wiegel had his arm in a cast. Cornforn was on crutches. I don't know what happened to him.

HUNGERFORD: It became apparent somewhat later that the police had had difficulty in discerning who was who, quite. Some innocent people were hurt, however I should like to point out that many of these injuries looked rather more severe than they were. The most superficial scalp wound will bleed profusely. I don't wish to appear indifferent to human suffering, but some of the newspaper pictures were deceptive. The police cannot be fairly blamed. Some members of the faculty were supporting the other side, and many, who claimed to be neutral, would not leave the area, got in the way, hampered the police in their work, and were injured through their own failure to cooperate with the authorities. Quite.

MIRSKY: Some of the Tappan Hall faculty wrote out a resolution, very strong, condemning the Administration, to be submitted to the Oberlin Auditorium meeting. What happened there I don't understand to this day. The hall was completely filled. The resolution was presented. There was a certain amount of debate and then the meeting just fell apart in confusion. There were some speeches against the resolution, but I didn't hear that many. It was like going into a bar and having someone slip you a mickey finn. The next thing I clearly remember is that three or four hundred faculty—just the remains of the meeting—were back in

Tappan Lounge. Arthur Wythe, who was in the chair at Oberlin, had simply adjourned the meeting. He got up in the middle of the debate on the resolution, announced the resolution was a mistake, said it was being withdrawn, adjourned the meeting, and walked out. I think he realized that if the resolution passed it would be truly revolutionary, and he didn't want to be a revolutionary. The reason I think he got away with it—imagine, just adjourning a meeting of fifteen hundred professors without so much as a how do you do—is that many of them weren't ready to pull down Hungerford at that moment.

It was already bright outside when Ellie entered Gilmore and felt the gloom of a building where night stayed after day had come. People everywhere were lying quietly on the floors in sleeping bags, under blankets or with coats over them, camping in the old building which Ellie felt was decorated in moldy classical revival, marble dadas that had yellowed, busts of wigged men in shell-shaped wall niches. The true Gilmore was unadorned, utilitarian, but Ellie's imagination took what ornamentation there was to buttress her fantasy of walking through some huge, dying place, a palace, a capitol overthrown.

She moved through several classrooms heavy with sleeping people. The sight of people sleeping where they ordinarily sat and took notes, this different use of customary space, seemed a sign of changes in the state of things, like photographs of soldiers with guns, dirty men in drawing rooms where they did not belong, pictures of schools turned into hospitals and opera houses used for constitutional assemblies. At the far end of one room a small group was talking while the rest slept. Ellie sat down near them, listened and dozed, listened and fell asleep.

First Boy: We have to set up a defense committee today. If the bust had come last night, we'd have been slaughtered.

Second Boy: They're not going to come. Last night proved it. They can't attack us without attacking the blacks, and they're afraid to do that.

First Girl: Our group is completely opposed to the defense committee. If the cops come, we want them to find us at work.

First Boy: You top-floor utopians are unreal. Your commune is staying up there waiting for the Holy Ghost, planning some kind of marvelous, restructured community. It's unconnected. You can't just stay in the attic, away from the rest of the building, not to mention the whole revolution.

First Girl: We're not outside the revolution. We're the revolution's meaning. We're the *real* radicals, the ones that are getting with each other and through that reaching out to see how a future can be designed.

First Boy: You're snobs.

Second Boy: Whatever's going to be changed about this university has to come through negotiation. I don't think a defense committee is necessary, but I do think you should take part in the discussions going on downstairs and not operate a separate commune.

First Girl: We don't have time to spend on the defense committee or political manipulations. No matter what happens, our work is the most important thing; it's the only thing that isn't hung up on skirmishes with the Administration. We're looking beyond.

First Boy: It's crazy. A bunch of art students, theologians, and architects up on the top floor with your charts and plans and principles. Don't you see, none of that can possibly make any difference unless you pay attention to what's happening on the first floor. You can't leave it to us to win your utopia for you.

Second Girl: There are people in this building with guns.

Second Boy: On the first floor. The radical hot dogs. Do they really have guns?

First Boy: They do not.

Second Girl: They do. In the anatomy lab. That's why they won't let anybody in there.

Second Boy: That *is* going to cause another bust. If the police hear about that, they *will* be back. Those guns have to leave the building.

Second Girl: God, this's scary.

Second Boy: The first floor has no right to bring guns into the building without consulting the rest of us.

First Boy: How's the first floor supposed to do that? The top-floor utopians talk only to God, and you second-floor social democrats refuse to believe there'll be another bust, so you won't talk about defense measures.

Second Boy: You talk like a hot dog. Are you a first-floornik?

First Boy: I'm in the stair caucus.

Second Boy: What's that? I haven't heard about that.

First Boy: We support the anatomy lab in principle but tactically we oppose armed resistance at this time. The stair caucus believes in guerrilla tactics, but not fighting the pigs from fixed positions because we don't have the firepower yet.

Second Girl: I don't believe it.

First Girl: We gave up attempting to communicate with the anatomy lab days ago. They're into the violence thing and they can't understand they're sinking down into the same level as the Administration.

First Boy: A revolution is a practical matter. It's the violent overthrow of the power structure. You have to think about it in practical terms—organization, money, guns—just like them.

First Girl: Yeah, just like them. We've had dozens of revolutions like that before. Let's have a different kind of revolution.

First Boy: Of the spirit?

First Girl: So? Is that bad?

First Boy: Secularized Christianity. Ethical Culture.

Quakerism. I hate non-violence. You religious ones are so calm, so sweet, so superior, *en rapport* with the Gas God.

First Girl: Talk about cocksure.

Second Girl: Don't we have to get together?

Second Boy: We do. All the communes and caucuses in the building should meet. We've got to decide what to do, and everybody's got to agree to do it. On the basis of majority rule. There's no other way.

First Boy: Thus speaks the social democrat. If we'd listened to you there'd be no revolution; we wouldn't be in this building, we'd all be way back in the petition-passing stage. The anatomy lab and the stair caucus are the van guard, and the vanguard educates the masses, especially the social democratic masses, by action.

Second Boy: We have to get together.

MIRSKY: I'm trying to remember what I felt Saturday afternoon. Tired of course. But were we hopeful? There was a period that night when we were somewhat hopeful. We had a glimmer. I think we felt that we had to keep trying. At the most there were five hundred people involved in the Faculty Emergency Committee, a minority of the University's instructional staff. FEC spanned a huge political spectrum, and there were people in it who wanted to use it, to make it take sides for the Administration, for the students. During that period I sensed a conviction among some of my colleagues that if the faculty, that is, FEC, joined one side or the other it would be decisive. I didn't believe so. I don't know. We were a minority, but I also like to think of us as the continuing spirit of the University, not the bomb factory university, or the radical new university, but the community of scholars and their apprentices we used to like to talk about in the bad, good old days when the radicals were in Moscow or the labor unions. FEC was made up of people who felt their vocations as teachers very strongly, people who wanted to save this place—Wiegel, Henry Wilson, Volanyi, my friend the astronomer.

We resumed our perpetual Tappan Lounge meeting. We were terribly tired, but we decided on one more effort at mediation. We would go to Nexus and then to the Administration at Rennecker. There were reports of movement out of Ripon with the blacks, and persistent rumors that Gilmore was "soft." If two of the buildings collapsed, or even threatened to collapse, Nexus might be feeling the pressure. Also, we believed we had a gimmick to get around the amnesty question. We knew Hungerford would never back down on that, so what we decided to propose was no amnesty but uniform punishment, all punishments the same. That way the leaders wouldn't be singled out for expulsion. We were assuming, naturally, that the Administration wouldn't be crazy enough to expel the two or three thousand students we believed were now in the buildings. I don't know if we had hope. The options were running out. Who else cared about this University?

YALDELL: By Saturday afternoon a lot of us were beginning to think that nobody besides the Administration cared about the University. I'm exaggerating. We got a lot of support from students, alumni, and from some of the faculty, but not enough to get a vote of confidence from the Oberlin Auditorium meeting. Afterward FEC got back together and became increasingly more obstructionist. They were dominated by the left, which manipulated their activities so as to attempt to make the Administration look as though it were refusing to be reasonable. The one good sign was the noises the Harvard-MIT urbanologists were bringing back from Ripon Hall. It began to sound like the black students would be willing to compromise. They were less radical, of course, and you had to sympathize with them.

The chancellor certainly did. We all understood there were special circumstances with the blacks.

Ellie awoke remembering the second boy had said "together . . . we have to get together." She remembered backward toward the beginning of the conversation as she went to find a bathroom, and when she did she saw that where it once said WOMEN, it now said LIBERATED. Inside there was a man who noted her fluster and said, "Nature. Don't be ashamed of your bodily functions. You're just going to tinkle."

"They're my bodily functions, not yours. So please leave."

"Social democrat?"

"Does it matter? Please leave."

He did, and as Ellie functioned bodily she thought of her family and what they would say if she told them. She decided the LIBERATED sign and the boy in the john would disturb her father more than the burning of Mitchell Memorial Library. The end of civilized conduct, but she'd taken it nicely, with assurance. Where had she gotten her assurance? From the revolution? Sil might be right. The revolution is liberation, learning how to order members of the anatomy lab out of the toilet. Silly, but how about overthrowing the government, isn't that silly, too? She combed her hair, wished she had a toothbrush, and put on her makeup. While she did, she discussed with herself why she was prettying her face, couldn't make up her mind, and walked up to the top-floor utopians. There were a great many of them, quiet people, self-restrained, but urging themselves against and through the confining membranes of their personalities. They were very emotional but in the lower registers the deeper tones quavered and cracked. Huge, long pauses in their conversations, between sentences and words, people pushing to get themselves out in the open.

"Know thyself, how?" a young man, probably a theologian, was saying. "Before this revolution I thought that meant you took stock of yourself, sat down and thought about yourself. I think now for me, maybe it's different for others, I know myself by a way of being with people. Before the revolution I was never with people. I was next to people. The people next door to my father's house, the people in the seat next to me at school, the people next to me in a line. Even making love I was next to the girl or I was in her, but I wasn't with her. We weren't together. You people, the people of the top-floor utopian commune, you are my family, you're my clan. I am with you. We are together."

Quiet in the room. No one hurried to be the next speaker.

"That's how I feel," someone said. There was no response, the group suspending itself in heavy quiet.

After a time the spirit moved someone else, who said, "I think we're together because we have committed ourselves to each other. I believe commitment is the active principle in people getting themselves together as individuals or as a family or a commune. We were brought up being told that the rituals we were taught were commitment; we learned to call what we did from fear and compulsion commitment. My father pays his income tax honestly and thinks he's a good citizen and a committed one, but I've heard him say, 'A man's a fool to cheat. The chances of getting caught are too high.' The same is true of our soldiers. They are compelled to serve, and when they do heroic things they do them to hide the true reasons they are soldiers from themselves. The revolution has given me my first chance to commit myself outside of ritual or force, freely and voluntarily, and that is why the top-floor commune is the most important experience in my life."

MIRSKY: Early Saturday evening FEC created two mediation committees, one to go to Ripon Hall and talk to the blacks, and the other, which I was on, to go back to Nexus to talk to Elias and the other members of the Student Revolutionary Action Committee. SRAC was supposed to have at least one representative from all the occupied buildings on it, but there was no one from Ripon there, nor, as far as I could determine, anyone from Gilmore. I don't remember the meeting too clearly. It was long, repetitive, and abusive. Elias was abusive. Once or twice we threatened to break it off, but Shapiro apologized for Elias. He kept accusing us of trying to split off Ripon Hall from the revolution. I was beginning to suspect that was what the Administration was trying to do. We called over to FEC and asked them to send a delegation over to the Administration to feel out what *was* going on. They did, but they weren't able to get in to see either Hungerford or McVey. They conferred with Associate Dean McTavish but learned nothing. From that point, it became increasingly difficult to get into Rennecker and talk to the officers of the University. I had the impression they were too taken up with planning tactics in their war room.

On the top floor the giving of testimony and public confession continued as Ellie listened, sometimes moved when she could apply the words to herself and sometimes indifferent when the ideas seemed too faint, too smudged, too introspective, or too much like her own to speak to her. She thought of Sil and Roger. They were not faint people. They didn't talk about commitment. They would be in the anatomy lab, first-floorniks.

"Are we being used?" someone asked, moving the topic off self-knowledge. "Are we being properly represented at Nexus? A lot of people say SDS is demanding things they know the Administration won't give so there'll be a bust."

"I don't think it's important, whether or not we're being used," the girl from the dawn conversation said. "I thought we'd decided we would not let ourselves get sidetracked into these political kinds of conversations."

"Yes, peace," another one put in.

"Love—"

"And non-violence."

Ellie left, going down to the second floor where the social democrats were talking, but they didn't interest her. She passed through the stair caucus and out the window to walk around the chaotic campus. It was night again, and the place was overrun with groups of antis and unattached radicals and disguised policemen and television crews and peace-keeping faculty. The largest crowd was around Fletcher, where the antis had bunched up to attack hideous Ignorance and restore the Mother of Wisdom, but they couldn't fight their way through the opposing crowd to get to the double-headed monster, who had the dribbling remains of books and test tubes on the lips of its mouth and skin pimpled with red assholes and toothed vaginas, which held burning cigarettes and ballpoint pens.

"I've been looking for you," the Supreme Cream said to her. He was there by her side, as though he'd fallen from a tree. "Shapiro and Roger have a message for you. You're supposed to go back to Gilmore and keep things together. Gilmore is schizophrenic and Fletcher Hall is paranoid and Ripon is alienated, but it's okay, Shapiro says."

"Cream, where are you going?" Ellie said to him as he made ready to take his great leaps off on some other errand.

"Gotta go. You're supposed to go to Gilmore, and oh! I almost forgot. You're supposed to get them to close up the building, keep everybody inside. Tonight or tomorrow I'll come and see you, Ellie."

"Thank you, Cream."

Ellie did as she was told, going back to Gilmore, thinking to herself that she was now part of the first floor. She was with them and Shapiro and Elias; they had assumed she was with them for a long time; now she decided. They had been trusting her, telling her their secrets, which she knew she didn't understand, and now they'd given her something to do that was political. It pleased her, although she didn't see how she could do it. She was too faint. Faint was the word—the second time she'd used it today. But she would try. The Supreme Cream was gentle, but he wasn't faint.

HUNGERFORD: The police intelligence received confirmed reports Saturday night that there were firearms in Gilmore Hall.

MCVEY: Till the very end we tried to remain accessible. We foreclosed no options. Until the minute of the actual beginning of the police action, we had an arrangement with them that permitted us to stop it, draw back. We knew as well as anyone that there could be the most terrible violence. We didn't want a confrontation. There was no doubt in our minds that it would be far worse than anything other campuses had experienced. For several hours we put great hope in what the Faculty Emergency Committee was doing, what Professor Mirsky was doing. And there were other leads, other hints and rumors of groups breaking off, wanting to negotiate. We tracked them all down.

MIRSKY: By late Saturday night or early Sunday morning, it seemed obvious to me that neither side was negotiating or even talking to us in good faith. Our amnesty formula was getting nowhere. SRAC wouldn't say yes or no. The most we could get out of them was a "pledge" to talk seriously about it if the Administration agreed. Elias just didn't believe there would be a bust, or, if he did, he didn't care. I tried to convince him and Shapiro that if they agreed to our formula and the Administration rejected it, a significant portion of the faculty would swing toward them. For our trouble we got tirades from Elias to the effect that the faculty should stop fooling itself and stop playing "the God-mediator" role. Like the U.N. Security Council, over and over, the faculty had to decide which side it was on. From the Administration we got—when we finally got in to see them—we got legalistic maybes. Imagine at this point these fools had the energy and shortsightedness to think up quibbles. Agreeing to the formula would be prejudging, it would imply the University had already convicted certain people of breaking regulations. It was unbelievable. I can't tell you. I can't tell you how we were in despair for this place.

WYTHE: I was the chairman of the FEC committee that was supposed to negotiate with Ripon Hall. We talked to Tully Haskins with that other fellow, B.J., listening—he didn't say anything—and I thought there was the beginning of some motion. But the Administration wouldn't see us above the level of McTavish. They said they were dealing with Ripon Hall through the Harvard-MIT urbanologists and we should, too. I felt there was nothing more my committee could do, and after reporting to the body I went home to bed. I was exhausted and disgusted. It was between two and three o'clock Sunday morning. I doubt if I'd stayed I would have accomplished anything. As it was, I was already so tired I was losing my temper with my colleagues. I knew my judgment had been affected by lack of sleep, and beneath that, as I say, I was in a fury. I went home, told my wife I was going to accept a position at Wisconsin I'd decided to decline. She made me a cocktail. I think it was one part demerol to one part gin. Anyway, I slept for fifteen hours at least and never returned to the campus, that is not

until Monday, when it was all over. I can't tell you the shock
I felt when I saw that once great campus . . . well, I'll take
the emotions I had at that moment to my grave.

Ellie crept in through the window at Gilmore, glanced
to the top floor of the building, and promised herself she
would stay inside and not come out until it was over. Something like a meeting of everybody in the building was happening. Gilmore had no auditorium, and its largest lecture
amphitheater couldn't accommodate all the people taking
part in the siege, even with the top-floor commune staying
upstairs and aloof, just as the anatomy lab refused to participate in any meeting which was not discussing violent
resistance.

YALDELL: We were positive that Gilmore was very, very
soft. That's ironic, isn't it?

The meeting was long, sometimes dull, and sometimes
close to hysterical. Once the chairman fell asleep. Later a
boy went crazy, running among the people begging them to
settle everything through prayer. The doctor from the
Medical Committee on Human Rights urged everybody to
stop smoking. "You can get along without sleep—I guess—
but not without oxygen." Someone said their real need was
for vitamins. A number of people agreed. "They won't do
you any good," the doctor argued. "We want them anyway," someone said, and the doctor replied, "Okay, whoever wants vitamins'll get vitamins, but as your medical
adviser I urge you to put a time limit on this meeting and
get some sleep."

That was debated, but the decision was uncertain. Somewhat later, Ellie gave her first public speech. It lasted for
twenty or thirty words; almost nobody heard it. She said
she thought everyone should either leave or agree to stay in

the building until things were settled. "It's not fair that people should have a voice in deciding something they're not willing to see through themselves," she said, but the debate wobbled off into a discussion of the terms they'd accept in return for leaving the building. About 3 A.M. it began to seem as if there were two major points of view. One group wanted to leave the matter to SRAC, and the other wanted to stay as long as the blacks did in Ripon Hall, accepting as satisfactory whatever they accepted. Before the question could be settled, someone in the room came up to the chairman and whispered in his ear. The chairman then told everybody that Professor Mirsky and a couple of other faculty members were outside and wanted to talk. After fifteen minutes of wrangling it was agreed to let them in.

Mirsky's voice was drying up on him. He spoke in an intermittent scratch. People kept shouting, "Louder! Louder!" but he couldn't talk louder. Finally it was arranged that he would whisper and the astronomer would repeat his words.

"You have to come out of here," he said, "The bust is coming. Believe me. THE BUST IS COMING. What you are doing is noble, but you've made your point. No matter what happens now, the University is going to have to concede to most if not all of the black demands in the coming months. You've won. Come out. If you stay you will learn that violence is the monopoly of the state. It will be used against you. You will be hurt."

It was inelegant and ineloquent. Mirsky knew it. As he looked at them resting, trying to think of something to say, they were shouting back at him, "Don't tell us about violence. Chicago, the Century Plaza, Oakland Army Terminal, Selma Bridge, The Pentagon, Columbia, San Francisco State!"

"You've won," he repeated himself. "Look, what are you doing? Waging total war? What are you doing? You can't stay here all the time. We've worked out a partial amnesty, no one expelled, your leaders won't accept it. Come out. Come out, please, it's over."

MIRSKY: The worst performance of my life. They couldn't hear and I couldn't talk. I had tears in my eyes. They were victims, truly sheep, sheep for the Sorelians who only wanted them as mutton chops, wanted them to be the cannon fodder that the poor things thought they would escape being by resisting. I couldn't reach them. Even if it had been possible to shake their confidence in Elias and the other Sorelians, I don't believe they would have come out until Ripon Hall did. I will always believe the blacks made a deal with the Administration, didn't tell the others and left them to their fate. How come no guns were found in the black building? No resistance in the black building, no one injured. They came out nicely and everywhere else there was bloodshed. There were many of my students in Gilmore. They were betrayed both by their leaders and the people they sacrificed themselves to help.

The campus quieted about dawn, and most of the people in the buildings slept till noon. Mirsky and his friends didn't. They took benzedrine, drank coffee, and met in Tappan Lounge preparing what they called "The Last Try." It laid down the terms of what FEC was able to agree was a fair solution, with a preamble saying the faculty had now decided to force both sides to take it and gave them till eight o'clock Sunday night.

YALDELL: FEC showed its true colors on Sunday when they came out openly in favor of the revolution. By then all the moderates had quit the group, except for a few like Mirsky, who was, if you'll pardon the expression, duped.

Ellie slept on the first floor. She pulled two chairs together and curled up on them with her coat over her shoulders. Even so she slept till she heard the liberated female from the night in front of Rennecker yelling that some boys should come and help with the food. Soon Shapiro and Roger came. Many collected to hear Roger say there would be no bust unless they invited it by disunion. The second-floor social democrats came downstairs to make known their suspicions that Roger and SDS didn't want negotiations.

"Why did you let that fink professor in here?" Roger answered them. "We've told them that negotiations are off until they promise not to try and split the movement any more. Gilmore is soft, so everybody says. The other buildings are together. You've got to be together."

It wasn't much of a speech for Roger. He was tired, too. And hurried. He left almost immediately. Shapiro stayed a little longer and answered some questions. He also urged them to close the building up, keep people inside, and get organized. When he left, a defense meeting was held on a just-in-case basis; but the social democrats' analysis coincided with what Roger said. A bust was impossible.

The building was closed. Everybody agreed to stay inside and no one else could come in unless he promised to stay. It was then decided to divide up Gilmore into zones of different kinds of resistance. The anatomy lab was the most violent resistance zone; the rest of the first-floorniks said they would resist less than very violently but more than symbolically, because it *was* revolution. The stair caucus said it would practice symbolic resistance (linking arms). The social democrats said this was suicidal, that the whole first floor was going to get itself killed and probably good riddance. They really didn't mean that, but realistically the only practical course to adopt was aggressive non-violence (going limp but agreeing to walk downstairs so as not to be dragged). The top-floor utopians were understood to have pledged themselves to absolute non-cooperation and non-violence.

When that was settled, the social democrats began agitating for the anatomy lab to change places with the top-floor utopians, because if the anatomy lab was going to be violent, really, really violent, they should be on top so the police could get everybody else out first without anyone being hurt. The utopians didn't want to move downstairs, and anyway it would be safer for the rest if the police cleared out the anatomy lab first.

YALDELL: We had instructions to call McVey if there was any sign that any building wanted to come out. I did nothing that afternoon and evening but go around the Square hoping to make a contact.

ROYSTERMAN: Everybody knew the bust would be Sunday night. It was a question of exactly when. By sundown there were thousands of police on all the streets adjoining the campus. Several National Guard units, too. You didn't know that? Somebody got a snapshot of Hungerford, McVey, and the Guard commander toasting each other in Pomfret's office just before the bust. It was Czechoslovakia a second time. The Administration never bargained in good faith. After the failure Friday night they only waited until they'd built up enough power to make sure the ghetto couldn't rise behind them.

During the sunny part of Sunday afternoon, famous radicals from the city came on campus and talked to people in the buildings. Some were famous writers whose names

Ellie knew. They were admitted to give their analysis of the situation. They were passed in through the window with the helmets and the boric acid solution (for MACE and tear gas burns) and gas masks, passed through to say that the students in France and Mexico were watching, that this represented the high mark of the revolution thus far, that there would be a bust (the power structure won't tolerate this any longer) and that there wouldn't be one (the blacks will burn down the city).

Roger reappeared and repeated, "There will be no creep scene tonight. No bust. Stay cool. Our nerve against theirs."

Ellie stayed out of the way of the liberated girl and helped in women's tasks. When someone would come in that she knew, she would run to be near them. Then she would stand and listen, reassured and calmed by them, not their words. Sil came in the window with a big hamper, crying out, "Fruit, brothers! Pineapples for our feast!" Ellie followed him into the anatomy lab, touching him too softly for him to feel her fingers as he put the hamper down and opened it. There were hand grenades inside. "Slob Child's coming with other goodies," he said, as he turned and saw Ellie and the look on her face. "Now you've seen, you've got to stay."

"Yes," she nodded.

MIRSKY: Ach! The faculty ultimatum. Nothing. It was nine o'clock before we remembered the deadline was over. There was nothing left of FEC, maybe a hundred men. We sent telegrams. Save us, save us. They went to anybody we could think of. Teddy Kennedy, President Nixon, U Thant, the Mayor, the Governor, I don't know who. The faculty was no longer a functioning body. The conservatives, the cowards, and the confused had gone home; the young radicals were going into the buildings. The remains—that was us—we did anything we could think of, you know, more petitions, tried to see Hungerford, couldn't, tried to get another meeting with Nexus. They told us, "Later tonight."

With dusk the mobs built up. They were especially thick and violent around Gilmore. Sil got through them another time, and Slob Child made it, but then the antis piled up in such numbers that they blockaded the building. Television camera crews put lights on the building and the heads of battling students.

HUNGERFORD: I personally prepared a statement which I later read over the campus radio station, asking everyone to clear the campus, including faculty. The statement said that anyone leaving the buildings at that time would not be subject to arrest, but if they stayed in the Square or in any of the buildings they would be arrested for trespassing.

Gilmore wasn't inaccessible to The Supreme Cream. He did amazing acrobatics from trees and second-floor windows, bringing heads of lettuce, hamburger for meatballs, bottles of wine, spaghetti. He had it in his head that they should eat an Italian dinner. After six or eight terrifying crossings, he said, "One more trip. For a loaf of French bread."

"That's enough, Cream," Sil said to him in an angry voice.

"No. Gotta have French bread."

"No! Goddamn," Sil repeated.

"Anyway, there's something I want to say to Shapiro. A little goodbye message before the siege starts," he said in a spirit of defiance that wasn't like him, and whipped out a window.

YALDELL: Even in that last hour, which was as frightening as anything I've seen, we were still trying. I ran into a boy, he was throwing up out of fear, who told me he'd gotten out of Gilmore and they definitely had guns in there. He'd seen them. I took him to McVey. He looked like he'd been shot himself when he heard this kid, and he ordered me out to see if we couldn't find somebody, anything.

The mobs began to move on the campus. They came up like the night wind, and the howling began again. Warbling in a sinuous near-and-far as it moved through gardens and little-used spots and then, growing, came out in the open spaces. In the anatomy lab, Ellie watched Sil cook The Supreme Cream's spaghetti on a bunsen burner.

MIRSKY: By that hour I was wearing a little sign pinned to my coat lapel that said, "Can't Talk. I've Given My Voice to the Revolution." But I got it back. The triumph of stress and anxiety over physical debilitation. My poor friend, the astronomer, and I found a heavy but vaguely portable power microphone and took it to what used to be Minerva. Somebody had changed it somehow. I'm sure of it. I remember thinking somehow, somebody had converted this statue into the figure of Ignorance. I was suffering from such lack of sleep I may have hallucinated. There was nothing left for us. We thought maybe with the loudspeaker we could calm people, and if the campus were calmed we could go back to try to persuade Hungerford to wait.

YALDELL: I got to talking with another kid who said he was from Gilmore, and that they were having a civil war in there because of the guns and that maybe, if we'd wait, they'd be coming out. I told the kid to wait while I tried to reach Blackie. Blackie said there was still time, but barely. He told me to bring the kid immediately, but when I got back he was gone.

MIRSKY: Nobody listened to us. Probably couldn't hear us. The noise. Awful. If they had, we were ridiculous. I kept repeating into the foolish thing, "I AM PROFESSOR MYRON MIRSKY. MANY OF YOU KNOW MY NAME. MANY OF YOU HAVE BEEN MY STUDENTS. I BEG YOU FOR YOURSELVES AND FOR THIS COMMUNITY WHICH WE ONCE LOVED AND WERE PART OF, PLEASE LEAVE, GO HOME, PLEASE. WE CAN HAVE A MASS MEETING TOMORROW. DEMOCRATIC PROCEDURES. CHANGE IS POSSIBLE. JUSTICE IS POSSIBLE. IT DOES NOT HAVE TO BE THIS WAY, DOESN'T HAVE TO BE THIS WAY. JUSTICE IS POSSIBLE."

And then, my God, it was silent. Nothing. In an instant I could hear a piece of newspaper blow on the steps in front of the statue. I could hear the footfalls of the last people running up those steps in criss-crossing diagonals. Running, I suppose, to get away. My friend and I had decided that if the moment came, we would go and stand in front of Gilmore, stand between the police and the students. It was the time now. Police were coming up softly and surrounding all the buildings. When we got to Gilmore, we heard music.

Inside the anatomy lab they were singing, "I Can't Get No Satisfaction . . . I try, I try, I try." Ellie tried to sing.

Outside, Mirsky saw a boy in a tree with a long something in his hand.

"Sniper!" shouted a policeman.

Shot

"It's The Cream!"

"NOW!" screamed Sil.

Explosion